GAMAILIS
and other tales from Stalin's Russia

GAMAILIS

AND OTHER
TALES FROM STALIN'S RUSSIA

by Vladimir Andreyev
translated by Fred P. Berry

HENRY REGNERY COMPANY
Chicago, 1963

Chicago 4, Illinois
Manufactured in the United States of America
LIBRARY OF CONGRESS CATALOGUE CARD NO. 63-9949

CONTENTS

NO, ONE CANNOT BUILD PARADISE with concrete. The bastion would be preserved, but it no longer had a message, nor an example to give to the world. Number One's regime had besmirched the ideal of the Social State even as some Mediaeval Popes had besmirched the ideal of a Christian Empire. The flag of the Revolution was at half-mast.

ARTHUR KOESTLER,
Darkness at Noon

GAMAILIS

I

KOLYMA

KOLYMA is the name of a river in lonely Yakutia, on the northeast edge of the Asiatic region of the Soviet Union. It cuts this territory from south to northeast for a distance of over two and one half thousand kilometers, and then empties into the East Siberian Sea. From the name of the Kolyma River, the whole region derives its name. It occupies an enormous expanse, bordered on the south by the Sea of Okhotsk and the Bering Sea, and on the east and north by the Chukotsk and East Siberian Seas. From there to Alaska is but a stretch of the hand.

The region is remote, wild, sparsely populated. It is a lonely *taiga* with many rocky mountains and hills. Along the river valleys wanders the sparse aboriginal population, consisting for the greater part of the Tungus and Yakut peoples, who subsist by hunting and the breeding of reindeer. The average population density is one person to fifty square kilometers. The villages of the natives are dispersed about the *taiga* hundreds of kilometers from one another. One seldom meets another human being in the *taiga*. There are no roads. The natives, when they travel, orient themselves by the mountains in the daytime, and at night by the stars. A person who wanders into the *taiga* without knowing the terrain and not possessing a compass, must surely perish.

The climate is cruel. The winter lasts from eight to ten months each year. The thermometer drops to minus sixty degrees and lower, and terrible snowstorms rage without interruption for several days at a time. In spring the frost thaws out, in places to a depth of as much as several meters. The short summer never succeeds in thawing the ground completely, however. Not for nothing is "Kolyma" known as the "region of eternal frost." In summer there are a very few hot, burning days.

The people have another name for this region. "Kolyma" is known as "the land of prisoners," and also with good reason. On "Kolyma" there are huge concentration camps. Although their official name is Northeast Corrective Labor Camps, among the people they are simply called "Kolyma." In the Soviet Union they sing this song:

Kto v Kolyme
ne pobyval,
Tot i gorya
ne vidal.
You don't know bitterness
If you haven't seen Kolyma.

These concentration camps are colloquially known as "Sevvostlag," but for official reference to them the special conventional name "Dal'stroy" (Far Eastern Construction) is used. This designation is intended to limit public knowledge of the fact that the labor of prisoners is used. During the years of Dal'stroy's existence there have passed through it nearly three million prisoners. By the labor of these people, imprisoned on "Kolyma," cities and villages have been erected, as well as rail and highway communication routes thousands of kilometers in length, factories and shops, air, sea and land strategic bases, mighty military shore fortifications and other projects. Gold is mined there in tremendous quantities, as well as other precious minerals, in which "Kolyma" has abundant reserves. The colossal achievements of this "building of communism" have been at the price of the lives of literally millions of prisoners over the years of Dal'stroy's existence.

At the time with which we are concerned, there were only five hundred thousand prisoners on "Kolyma." At that time, in addition to gold mining operations, primitive villages and paved roads were being constructed, extending from the Bay of Nagaev on the Sea of Okhotsk toward the mouth of the Kolyma River. Ultimately it was contemplated to extend the road construction to the Bay of Ambarchik, and to Anadyr' and Yakutsk. Five hundred kilometers of road had already been laid. The road came to an end at Seimchan, the most distant settlement at that time. Beyond lay the *taiga*—wild, unconquered.

With the beginning of the summer, small geological prospecting groups, consisting of engineer-prisoners, technicians and workers, were thrown each year hundreds of kilometers into the depth of the *taiga*. For a few months, until the coming of the first snow, they prospected, searching for ores. They looked for gold deposits, for silver, copper, lead, zinc, wolfram, iron, mica, graphite, coal and other valuable minerals. These geologic prospecting parties were generally led by one or two volunteer engineers. An armed guard of several persons would be attached to them. Such parties were provided with reserves of food and of whatever else was necessary for extended work in the lonely *taiga*.

At that time, just as now, gold was mined there, and in such quantity that it exceeded all advance calculations. Over a period of several years the plans were annually doubled, and over-fulfilled, every year. Just the same, for pilfering of gold, in the fields or in the vaults, the guilty parties were shot. Every year, with the opening of navigation, tons of the precious metal were sent to Moscow under heavy guard, and in exchange, from the Kremlin were sent little Morocco boxes with medals, for the decoration of the engineers and the Chekists, those "builders of Socialism," for successful fulfillment of the assignments of the Party and government—for the transformation of human raw material into gold. In those days, according to unofficial reckonings of informed persons, one kilogram of gold mined on "Kolyma" cost the lives of fifteen prisoners. The perishing of literally millions of prisoners over the years of developing and building "Kolyma" was a cost in the mining of the gold to which the Party and the government paid no attention. They approved and encouraged in every way the directors of the Kolyma project. Every year, with the opening of navigation, caravans of ocean-going steamships moored in the Bay of Nagaev, bringing to "Kolyma" new hundreds of thousands of prisoners.

The city of Magadan, located three kilometers from the Bay, is the administrative center of "Dal'stroy," and all the central headquarters of the various camps are located there. The chief of Dal'stroy at the time of which we are speaking was one Edward Berzin, nicknamed "The Beard." He was a mighty Chekist, an executive with unrestricted power. He had unlimited rule over the entire Kolyma region, and was subordinate only to the People's Commissar for Internal Affairs of the USSR Yagoda, and to the Politburo of the Central Committee of the All-Union Communist Party (Bolsheviks).

II

EXTRAORDINARY INCIDENT

The Kolyma region, after a long severe winter, was coming to life, was transforming itself under the rays of the spring sun, was covering itself with fresh young grass. . . . Only the tops of the mountains and certain hills remained covered with white caps of snow, and in some places grey snowdrifts still stubbornly remained in the mountainous ravines, slowly dissolving in the warm air.

In Magadan, at the central radio station Dal'stroy, there had just been received an urgent, encoded priority radiogram from Seimchan, the most distant outpost of the camp at that time, located five hundred kilometers from Magadan. On the narrow tape unintelligible five-figure groups appeared. The radio operator on duty was long accustomed to such ciphers, which were transmitted in great quantity every day. They usually aroused in him no curiosity whatsoever. He would mechanically receive them, devoting his entire attention to ensure against making an error. But this radiogram, from the very first signals received, aroused in him interest, and uneasiness.

00333 . . . 00333 . . . 00333 . . . This group of ciphers was repeated three times, and then the string of figures continued on . . . 00333 is the conventional symbol known to all Soviet radiomen. It signifies: "Top Secret–extraordinary incident." Radiograms identified by such a symbol must be immediately handed over, day or night, to the person to whom they are addressed, personally. Delay in the delivery of such a radiogram results in the guilty party's being brought before a court, and faced with imprisonment.

Within a few minutes this radiogram was already in the hands of Berzin, the chief of Dal'stroy. It carried important news. In the depth of the *taiga*, in the Taskan district south-east of the Charsky range, Geologic Prospecting Group Number 54 was working. This group was headed by an engineer-geologist and his assistant. Both were young, energetic persons, both were members of the Communist Party, and had recently come voluntarily to "Kolyma," upon call of the Party after completion of their training at the Geological Institute, in order to help in the development of this wild remote district of the country.

In this geologic party were several prisoner engineer-geologists and technicians, and ten workers who also were prisoners. The group was guarded by eight soldiers, armed with rifles and pistols. Among the prisoners was one engineer-geologist, named Gamailis, sentenced to ten years confinement on "Kolyma" for anti-Communist activity. The prisoners, under Gamailis' leadership, having agreed among themselves, fell upon the guard at night, seized their weapons, destroyed those who resisted, and concealed themselves in the *taiga*. They had seized and taken with them all of the group's supplies, and the pack horses as well. Only two had been able to save themselves–the chief engineer, Petrov, and a soldier, Rozanov, who was wounded in the arm. Petrov and Rozanov had wandered for ten days about the *taiga*, trying to reach some inhabited point. Finally, exhausted from hunger and fatigue, they came upon a camp settlement and told what had happened. Mounted groups of the guard, with search dogs, were sent to the scene of the incident in pursuit of the fugitives. Engineer Petrov and the soldier Rozanov were sent to the hospital in a critical condition. All of this was contained in the flash radiogram.

Not more than a half hour after receipt of this communication, the individuals who were responsible for the operation of "Kolyma" gathered in the office of Berzin, Chief of Dal'stroy. Like Berzin himself, all the others attending the meeting were disturbed by this incident. The murder and disarming of soldiers of the guard . . . an armed escape—this was a scandalous incident, and one demanding the application of firm measures for its liquidation, and severe punishment of the fugitives. However, the fugitives were in possession of supplies, and had also seized pack horses. They were in a position to sustain themselves for a considerable time. They had maps, even if only the most primitive type, and compasses, binoculars, documents and military uniforms which they had seized from the murdered soldiers. Finally, they possessed weapons and ammunition for protection against beasts of prey, usually found in abundance in the *taiga.* They could offer serious opposition in the event of a meeting with any guard which might be sent to capture them.

But where would they go? They could not go to the south or to the east; in this direction lay the territory of the concentration camps, the territory of Dal'stroy. Would they go north, to the coast of the East Siberian Sea? But to accomplish this they would have to trek a distance of more than a thousand kilometers through the lonely, almost uninhabited *taiga,* without roads in a mountainous terrain. Even though equipped with a map and compass they would not be able to get through to the coast in less than three months, and by this time the winter would find them, with its snowstorms and intense cold—meaning death. To go toward the most inhabited area, toward Yakutsk? But here too they would have to overcome the difficulties of a similar journey of at least a thousand kilometers, also through the *taiga*, until they could break through to settled points. Once again the winter would find them in the *taiga*, and by that time their escape would be known in the settled points, and they would be apprehended there. The officials were perplexed, and could not understand why this group of prisoners had made this hopeless escape, and what was more, complicated it with murder and disarming of the guard. The fugitives must certainly have understood that in case they were caught the death penalty awaited them. What were they thinking and what were they hoping for? The whole affair was incomprehensible.

The fact that the fugitives would not get away was obvious, but another question disturbed the high command. These fifteen men, understanding the inevitability of their death, would stop at nothing in order to prolong their life to the last possible minute. In any attempt to seize them they could be expected, in their desperation, to fight to the last breath. Not one of them would give himself up, without opposition to the authorities, in order to undergo a torturing interrogation and to be shot. . . .

There was still another question, which disturbed Berzin personally. According to existing regulations an immediate report to Moscow by radio was mandatory in every case of escape, particularly one involving an attack on the guard, and murder. But already ten days had elapsed since the time of the incident, and it had only now become known. Berzin, as chief of Dal'stroy, was personally responsible to Moscow for this. Indeed, to report at this late date concerning this outrageous flight, and to admit that the fugitives had gotten away, this Berzin did not want to do. This offended his professional Chekist ego. At the conference they decided for the time being to report nothing to Moscow, and to wait a few days, after having first taken all possible measures to apprehend the fugitives. It was decided to warn the administration of that section of the camp from which the escape had been accomplished, and the commander of the same unit of the guard, that they would be subject to the most severe punitive measures unless the fugitives were caught in the very shortest time. They reckoned that, once the escape had been liquidated, they would report immediately to Moscow concerning the matter, and also that the fugitives had been apprehended. They could explain the tardiness of the report by the difficulty of communication, the great territory of the camp, the isolation of the camp's outposts in the *taiga*, the absence of telephone communication between points, and so forth. Berzin ordered the immediate arrest of the engineer and the wounded soldier Rozanov, whose good luck had saved them from death, and commanded that they be taken under guard to Magadan and brought before a court as an example to others, for negligence in having permitted the armed escape of the prisoners.

The meeting presently came to an end, and soon the same radio operator on duty at the central radio station in Magadan, deferring all routine radiograms, sent in cipher a long message in the mysterious five figure groups, which again began with 00333 . . . 00333 . . . 00333 . . . Berzin's urgent order was sent out.

III

UNFORESEEN COMPLICATIONS

Two weeks passed. From the *taiga* came very discomforting reports. Several mounted groups had been thrown into the search, taken from the *taiga* guard detachments. Despite all efforts no trace of the fugitives could be found. The *taiga* is vast; there are no roads, and almost no points of habitation, except for the infrequent small settlements of the nomadic natives, separated from each other by distances of 150-200 kilometers and more. The fugitives were moving steadily over the terrain. The *taiga* was hiding them safely, not betraying the secret of their whereabouts. "They have one road, and we have forty," said the soldiers of the guard among themselves, after having sought them in vain in the *taiga*.

The high command in Magadan began to be seriously disturbed. The report to Moscow had still not been dispatched, in the full hope that the fugitives would soon be apprehended, if not today, then tomorrow. Strict orders were sent into the *taiga*, as well as warnings and threats. The command in the *taiga* sections of the camp became nervous. More and more forces of the guard were thrown into the search, doing everything possible, fearing lest they fail. The commanders of the guard, having no peace themselves, day or night, gave none to their subordinates. The fugitives could not be found, however.

Suddenly, an enciphered priority government radiogram, quite unexpected, addressed to Berzin, arrived from Moscow. Its text was laconic, dry, threatening:

PRIORITY. OFFICIAL.
Dal'stroy. For Berzin.

Why no report re attack on guard and escape Gamailis. Who is guilty? Shall wait twenty-four hours.

Yagoda.

Berzin knew very well what was meant by the question, "Who is guilty?" It meant, who was guilty of permitting the armed escape of the counter-revolutionaries from the camp. It meant, who was guilty of concealing the matter, and not reporting it promptly to Moscow. Berzin could at will easily find persons guilty of having permitted the escape. Engineer Petrov and the soldier Rozanov would do, or even the commander of the guard and the other officials of the administration, who were directly accountable for the guarding of the prisoners. But for the absence of a report concerning the matter to Moscow, only Berzin himself could be held accountable.

Berzin understood very well what the phrase meant, "Shall wait twenty-four hours." This meant that, after a day and a night, regardless of whether an answer were received or not, a decision would be taken with regard to Berzin. This decision would be taken in the Politburo, by Stalin himself. Thereafter any attempt at explanation or justification would be useless, no matter how well-founded it might be. The dry, severe tone of the radiogram made quite plain that the matter might entail for Berzin the most serious consequences. His anxiety was aggravated by the fact that, although he enjoyed patronage from several members of the Politburo of the Central Committee of the Party, his relationship with the People's Commissar for Internal Affairs Yagoda was strained, even inimical, as a result of intrigue and Chekist rivalry for power. Yagoda attempted at all possible occasions to discredit him before the Politburo, and even though Berzin enjoyed authority and popularity with Stalin himself, Yagoda's influence still made itself felt.

That very same day Berzin, after confiding his intent only with his very closest and most trusted associates, sent to Moscow the following enciphered radiogram:

PRIORITY. OFFICIAL.
Moscow. For People's Commissar for Internal Affairs Yagoda.

Flight Gamailis unsuccessful. Full details by special report.

Berzin.

For Berzin it was very risky to send such a radiogram, but he had to forestall a decision in Moscow against him, and win time. He understood the complications which could arise for him, and he did everything possible in order to cover himself from possible unpleasantness. After having sent his reply to Moscow, Berzin gave an order to the Chief of the Operative Section of State Security, one Yakubovsky, and to the Procuror, named Nazarov, who belonged to the circle of his closest intimates, and who were especially trusted by him. The order was as follows: bring to an immediate conclusion the judicial inquiry concerning Petrov and the soldier Rozanov. Charge them both as accomplices of Gamailis and the other prisoners in disarming and murdering the guard members and others with the purpose of accomplishing an escape with stolen gold across the border. In this way "guilty parties" were found who could be accorded the severe punishment which they "deserved." Furthermore, the sole witnesses of what had actually transpired were thus conveniently eliminated.

Berzin's greatest problem had still not been solved, however. Gamailis and his group remained at large and there seemed to be no hope whatsoever of catching them in the immediate future. It was imperative that Gamailis and his accomplices be apprehended or destroyed in the very shortest possible time. If apprehended, they must be shot, not only because of the assault of the guard and attempted escape, but also, and much more important, because the destruction of all of them was necessary in Berzin's personal interest in connection with his misunderstanding with People's Commissar for Internal Affairs Yagoda. Berzin was obliged at all costs to make good the words of his radiogram, "Flight Gamailis unsuccessful."

He reasoned that if Gamailis and his group could be apprehended, even if it be several weeks after the occurrence of the escape, then Berzin would be technically correct in having claimed that it was unsuccessful, since the fugitives, even though they might have covered hundreds of kilometers, were still on the territory of Dal'stroy, still within Berzin's jurisdiction. If necessary, the dates could be adjusted to fit the circumstances. It would be difficult to check them; indeed it would not be worthwhile for anyone to attempt to do so.

In this way Berzin hoped to refute the information which had been received in Moscow by Yagoda. But until Gamailis was caught, the danger remained that he might get out of the territory of Dal'stroy, and that irreparable complications and unpleasantness for Berzin would result. But it was not easy to apprehend Gamailis as soon as Berzin wanted. Even Berzin's unrestricted powers in the Kolyma region turned out to be inadequate for this task. His special plenipotentiary power from Party and government did not help him, either. The command of Berzin, which under other circumstances settled the fate of millions of people in his power, was of no help to him here. Gamailis, even if certainly doomed, was for the moment at least, beyond the reach of the absolute ruler of "Kolyma."

There was still another question, one which caused Berzin considerable uneasiness. How did Moscow become aware of Gamailis' escape? Who had dared to dispatch this information without his knowledge and permission? According to a strictly established regulation, all radiograms from Magadan to the "Big Country," as the rest of the USSR was known on "Kolyma," could be dispatched only with Berzin's permission. They were subjected to the strictest censorship. Especially important radiograms, and those pertaining to governmental matters, could be sent only with Berzin's personal signature. There could have been absolutely no other means of communication, since not a single ship had left the Bay of Nagaev since the time of the incident, and at that time air communication did not yet exist. It was vitally necessary for Berzin to know precisely what information had been sent to Moscow, and the time of its dispatch. He would have to frame his explanations around this, and if it appeared necessary, also create any "situation" required for his report to Moscow.

The central radio station of Dal'stroy in Magadan was the only point which could have direct communication with Moscow. Meticulous investigation conducted at Berzin's order did not provide the results needed. The application of clandestine operational techniques also proved fruitless. The mighty Berzin's all-powerful Chekist apparatus turned out to be ineffectual. Berzin was enraged by his impotence. He cancelled until further notice the clearance of all ships from the Bay of Nagaev to Vladivostok. He ordered strict control of radio communication.

And then, quite by accident, the mysterious riddle was solved. It was so simple, as it turned out, that nobody had considered it. On "Kolyma," in addition to Dal'stroy, there was the 61st Okhotsk-Kolyma Border Detachment, whose headquarters was also located in Magadan. This detachment was preparing for a very important inspection by the Main Administration of Border Troops of the NKVD. A special commission had already arrived from Moscow to conduct the inspection. This was an exceptionally important matter for the local detachment. Naturally Gamailis' escape had alerted not only the administration and guard of the camps, but the border troops as well. For them also there would be serious consequences, if Gamailis and his group succeeded in penetrating the border sector which was under their care. In connection with the escape the border units intensified their controls, even though it was not very likely that the fugitives would succeed in making their way as far as the seacoast. Such intensified activity required unusual commitments of troops for duty. It was quite infeasible during such a state of alert to draw up the troops for a formal inspection. By agreement with the inspector who had arrived from Moscow with the commission, Orlov, commander of the border detachment, arranged to postpone the inspection until the fugitive Gamailis could be liquidated. Both Orlov and the inspector, however, were reluctant to take upon themselves the responsibility for an independent postponement of the inspection for even the briefest period without permission from Moscow. Therefore a special radiogram, enciphered in the special code of the border troops, was sent to Moscow, to the Administration of Border Troops of the NKVD. In the radiogram it was stated that, in view of the flight of Gamailis with a group of prisoners, it was necessary for the border detachment to undertake to strengthen the guard of the border. Permission was requested to postpone the inspection. This radiogram was sent to Moscow in the full belief that the news of Gamailis' escape had already reached Moscow, since it was known that Berzin was under a standing requirement to report it. Radiograms from the border detachment were not subject to Berzin's censorship, since the code was different.

Frenovsky, Chief of the Main Administration of Border Troops, was also a Deputy Commissar of Internal Affairs of the USSR. He was in general very inimically disposed toward Berzin. In the present case, however, he suspected nothing special upon receiving Orlov's radiogram, and simply reported it as a routine matter to Yagoda. Prior to this Yagoda had known nothing of Gamailis' escape. He was incensed by the fact that he had found out about it, not from Berzin, but from the border troops. Yagoda raged; Frenovsky exulted. Berzin's difficulties suited his interests as well as those of Yagoda. It was not until several days after the receipt of the first radiogram from Moscow that Berzin found out about these details, and then only when Orlov, in the hope of gaining approval and favor from the high-ranking Chekist, informed Berzin that he had received from Moscow an affirmative reply to his request for permission to postpone the inspection, and that as a result Berzin could rest assured that the border would be sealed against Gamailis. Berzin flew into a rabid fury. He was ready to kill Orlov.

As simply as that, was the mystery of Moscow's knowledge of the incident explained. Berzin now knew what he had to do.

We must return now to the trying day when Berzin received the radiogram from Moscow with the inquiry concerning Gamailis' escape. That very day Berzin had called to his office the Chief of the Operative-Chekist Department Yakubovsky and had given him the order to organize immediately a detachment of picked soldiers and officers of the guard, about two hundred strong, and to select twenty of the best search dogs. Yakubovsky was to take command of the detachment and move out not later than dawn of the following day to the end of the road, which at that time extended about five hundred kilometers. There he was to requisition from the chief of the most outlying *taiga* section whatever quantities of pack and saddle horses, and supplies, were necessary, as well as a selection of Yakuts who knew the terrain well, and who spoke Russian. Upon arrival in the zone of action the detachment was to be broken down into groups of twenty to twenty-five men with indigenous guides and search dogs, and these groups were to be dispatched at forced march into the *taiga* in pursuit of Gamailis, taking the direction of his most likely avenue of flight. If the fugitives were not overtaken, a diligent search in the *taiga* was to be undertaken. All search groups dispatched previously were, whenever encountered, to be added to Yakubovsky's forces. The aid of the population was to be enlisted in a widespread participation in the search. Premiums and medals were to be promised to the indigenous population for information as to the whereabouts of the fugitives. The natives were to be informed that the fugitives were bandits, subsisting by murder and plundering.

Berzin authorized Yakubovsky to act in his name and gave him full discretionary powers. He ordered him to spare no means to achieve the objective. In conclusion, Berzin ordered, "Get Gamailis and his accomplices within ten days. Inform all the soldiers and officers that they will be held responsible before the judicial commission if Gamailis is not caught dead or alive. If you succeed—there will be decorations."

Before dawn on the following day, a column of trucks left Magadan at full speed along the auto highway into the *taiga*. In the two final trucks the dogs barked uneasily, and were soothed by their handlers. In the fore, in a light automobile, rode Yakubovsky. Toward evening of the same day the auto column came up to the point where the road came to an end. Beyond stretched the trackless *taiga*. In the camp settlement, saddled horses were already standing in waiting. Several dozen horses were standing with packs filled with supplies. A little to one side fifteen Yakut guides were waiting, holding on tethers their small, shaggy, long-maned horses with quaint saddles. After about two hours of preparation, the detachment, divided into several groups, moved in a long file along the rocky wasteland, hidden in the *taiga* which had become black in the evening gloom. Nothing broke the silence except the clopping of the horses' hoofs. The men rode in silence. They all had but one thought: What's ahead? Berzin's decorations, or the prison of "Kolyma"—or perhaps, death in the coming battle.

IV

THE SEARCH

A week passed. In the depth of the *taiga* a field headquarters was set up for the direction of the search. Yakubovsky stationed himself there. Several hundred soldiers of the local guards, and local native population who lived in the district within a radius of 250 kilometers, were attached to them. Large numbers of mounted search groups with dogs, detaching themselves from the main force, scoured the *taiga.* Cutters and motor boats bearing armed men moved along the rivers. From time to time airplanes of Dal'stroy soared over the *taiga* at low levels, observing the terrain, seeking out the fugitives. They did not maintain direct contact with the search groups which were scattered over the great territory, but tossed out food packages and received reports, which they delivered in Magadan to Berzin, hundreds of kilometers away. There were no portable radio transmitters.

Special delegations were sent to all native villages, no matter how small or remote, offering prizes for assistance in the search. They brought packages filled with spirits, tobacco, clothing, powder, shot, and trinkets. These items cost little, but were highly prized by the natives. Among the native population rumors were circulated about the savage band of Gamailis, which even killed women and children, plundered the people, burned the huts, destroyed the livestock. In one of the Yakut villages the supply of pelts, which had been laid away by the Yakuts in a storehouse, was stolen. Horses from the village disappeared, and a large stock of hay was set afire.

Gamailis and his people could not have done these things, since he had not been in the district where they occurred, as was later made clear. These were provocatory acts of Yakubovsky, perpetrated with the aim of evoking hatred toward Gamailis, and to make the natives eager to cooperate in the search. The simple natives believed the men in uniform, who generously gave away packages of makhorka, tea pressed into little blocks, boxes of matches, spirits, glittering trinkets—all completely unobtainable in the *taiga*. A hatred of the unknown evil-doers spread about the *taiga* with unbelievable speed, as did the news of the prizes for their capture. "The *taiga* has big ears," say the Yakuts. The news quickly reached the very loneliest corners of the wilderness, by mysterious paths. The old people, the young and the half-grown, and even the women searched through the *taiga* with their old Berdan rifles, loaded with lead bullets the thickness of a finger. The Yakut can hit a squirrel in the eye at a hundred meters. He knows the value of the pelt, and how to avoid spoiling it. He knows the value of the bullet, and how to avoid wasting it. He knows that for a hundred squirrel pelts he can get a pound of tobacco from the Russians at the trading stations far away. But for the capture of an evil-doer he can get a hundred pounds of tobacco with one bullet. The "rich, good Russians," who had come from far away to protect the Yakuts from the bandits, had said so. The Yakut is hard-working and honest. He does not tolerate evil; he destroys it. He will kill the "evil-doer." He will save his home, his livestock, his family, and the good Russian will pay him a magnificent reward. Day and night the Yakut noiselessly steals through the *taiga*, sharply looking out, peering about, harkening to every rustle. . . .

In spite of all measures however, no one was able to determine the whereabouts of Gamailis. The period set by Berzin was running out. But then suddenly one day in the field headquarters of the search, located on the Berelekh River, a Yakut galloped in on an exhausted horse. Bound to his breast was a bundle wrapped in tree bark and secured by sinews. The Yakut was in a condition of great excitement and alarm. In the last two days he had covered a distance of about two hundred kilometers on his little horse. In the package he carried was a report from the commander of one of the search groups operating along the Elik River.

The report informed that not far from the Elik River, on the slope of a mountain, a bivouac of Geological Party No. 8 had been discovered. This party consisted of twenty-two persons; engineers, technicians and workers. They were all prisoners, except for one engineer-geologist, the chief of the party. Attached to them was a guard of twelve soldiers. The party had several pack horses, and supplies necessary for a period of three months. They all knew about Gamailis' flight with the other prisoners, and about the searches. For this reason they always took precautionary measures. Two days previously, in the evening, when the geological party had finished its daily work and was in bivouac, resting, several shots were fired from the side of the mountain. Two soldiers were killed. There was an exchange of fire which lasted about an hour, as a result of which several soldiers and prisoners were killed or wounded. The chief of the geological party was also killed. In the commotion everybody scattered through the woods in various directions. The three soldiers of the guard who were left alive fled, and made their way back to the Yakut village of Elik, which was located ten or twelve kilometers from the scene of the incident. In the village they met a mounted search group of twenty persons with two dogs. When they learned what had happened, the group took off immediately at a gallop toward the scene of the recent skirmish.

Upon arrival at the destroyed bivouac of Geologic Party No. 8, they discovered the bodies of the soldiers, the chief of the party and of several prisoners. The bodies of the soldiers had been stripped of their uniforms, weapons and ammunition. The attackers had also seized the pack horses, reserves of provisions, stocks of ammunition, among which were hand grenades, compasses, binoculars, maps and documents. Upon inspection of the surrounding terrain were found two wounded soldiers with their weapons, who had hidden themselves in the thick underbrush on the river bank. All the remaining prisoners of the geological party had evidently run off into the forest or joined Gamailis' group. Dogs were put to a search of the terrain, but there nobody else could be found. The dogs took up the pursuit and energetically set off into the depths of the forest in the direction away from the river, through a saddle in the mountains. Mounted soldiers rode after them. After having covered about fifteen kilometers the mounted group came out onto a large open clearing at the foot of a rocky height. Dusk was setting in. The dogs kept straining onward in hot pursuit; the horsemen rode relentlessly after them. Beyond the saddle the trail split in two. One turned sharply to one side, up the mountain. The other went along the valley. The dogs were becoming very excited; they began to bark and scramble up the sharp slopes. And then, from behind the rocks shots were fired from several rifles. Hand grenades flew into the midst of the soldiers. Confusion developed among them, they fell back into the forest in disorder. Several soldiers, whose horses had been killed under them, fled on foot. The wounded crawled behind cover. A few killed and severely wounded soldiers and horses remained on the spot. The dogs, who had been freed from their leashes, threw themselves on Gamailis' fighting men behind the cover of the rocks, but they were shot almost point-blank. The horses of the killed and wounded rushed madly about the clearing. The soldiers who remained alive, after withdrawing into the forest, began to return the fire, but after a short exchange, they collected the wounded and withdrew, making their way to the village of Elik, where they arrived toward morning.

All this had happened two days ago. This is what Yakubovsky's headquarters was able to learn from the Yakut's report. The news caused considerable uneasiness. Despite the fact that night was approaching, messengers were dispatched in all directions. Mounted soldiers were sent in twos and threes and almost all the Yakuts who were at the headquarters—the interpreters and guides—were also sent out. From the village of Berelekh, located near Yakubovsky's headquarters, almost all the adult population was also sent out in various directions to ascertain the location of "Gamailis' band."

The local population, embittered, and generously paid by Yakubovsky, eagerly and conscientiously executed the missions assigned them, and took an active part in the liquidation of Gamailis and his group. In the villages of the Yakuts a terrible uneasiness reigned. The people, when going to sleep at night, kept their loaded rifles by their sides.

Day and night armed Yakuts guarded the villages and the pastures of their livestock, in anticipation of an attack by Gamailis. Even children took part in the vigil.

Yakubovsky decided to concentrate all the search groups operating in the *taiga* in that district where Gamailis had been most recently encountered. In the headquarters hundreds of pennants with bright long cloth streamers were hastily prepared. Wrapped in the pennants were Yakubovsky's orders regarding further actions of the search groups. The pennants were turned over to the first airplane which arrived. The pilot scattered them from the air about the *taiga* whenever search groups were seen. That evening Yakubovsky rode with his staff out to the village of Elik, in order to organize from there the pursuit of Gamailis and his men, from the fresh trail. A report was dispatched to Berzin by airplane. It was short: "We have found Gamailis' trail in the Elik district. There was an engagement. We are in pursuit."

Airplanes patrolled over the district where Gamailis was presumed to be. Although the air patrols gave little results, since Gamailis concealed himself from them in the *taiga* and it was difficult to discover him, even from a low altitude, the patrolling continued all the same. It was designed to keep Gamailis under pressure, to force him to avoid open places, which would of course slow his movement. After three days and nights, Yakubovsky with his staff was already on the Elik river, at the place where the bivouac of Geological Party No. 8 had stood.

But now a few words must be said about what the mounted group had been doing since its encounter with Gamailis, after the report of the incident had been sent to Yakubovsky. On the day following the engagement the commander of the group, who had been wounded in the shoulder, assembled all his remaining men, even the slightly wounded, drafted several Yakuts from the village of Elik, and in this manner composed a mounted group of twenty-three men. This group rode out to the place where the encounter had taken place the day before. Upon carefully examining the terrain, they discovered the trail once more, and they set off to follow it. Toward evening, on coming up to the Berelekh River, they ran across the site of a recent halt. On the bank were the traces of campfires, empty food cans and remnants of food. Several sawn-off trees, lopped-off branches and chips scattered about testified to the fact that rafts had been built. Bloody rags were found also, indicating that wounds had been dressed. It was clear that Gamailis' group had been here not more than a few hours ago. It was evident that only a portion of his men were sailing down the river on the rafts which they had built, since the tracks of men and horses were also seen leading off along the river.

With the dawn the mounted group set off quickly along the trail. After about fifteen kilometers they came to a point where the depth of the river at the bank was not more than half a meter. There they saw the horses' tracks leading into the water in order to cover the trail. They searched for the trail until late in the evening, and then passed the night by the river. On the following day they examined the river bank further, but found nothing, except a freshly covered grave. When they opened it they found a bandaged engineer prisoner of Geological Party No. 8, who had died of wounds. He was recognized by a soldier who had known him well. After several days the mounted group returned to the village of Elik, where it found the field headquarters of Yakubovsky. This latest search, even though it had not produced results, did provide very important data concerning Gamailis' movement down the Berelekh River. Evidently he had decided to move in the direction of the Sea of Okhotsk. It was now June, and as early as the end of September, severe winter weather would set in. The very closest point of escape from Soviet soil lay in precisely the direction which Gamailis had chosen.

Gamailis' forces were reckoned approximately. His group consisted of twenty-three to twenty-five persons. He possessed about twenty military rifles, six or eight pistols, several hunting rifles, about two thousand rounds of ammunition and several hand grenades. He was capable of serious resistance.

Yakubovsky concentrated all his forces in the Elik-Berelekh-Loshkalak district, and organized security measures within a radius of two hundred kilometers. Surround Gamailis, catch him in a ring, capture or destroy him. This was the mission. Through the *taiga*, slowly, relentlessly, the many mounted and foot soldiers pressed onward toward the region where Gamailis was, surrounding him from all sides. . . .

V

THE PURSUIT

Smoothly, neatly, with a gently pattering motor, the cutter "Kavasaki" slipped over the surface of the Berelekh River. From the small mast fluttered a white square banner with blue edging, bearing the legend "Dal'stroy." The sun was soaring, the heat unendurable. On the forward deck of the cutter a machinegun was mounted. Standing by the machinegun, dressed in sport trunks, with a pistol in a shoulder holster and with his head wrapped in a towel, the machinegunner was lost in revery. In the small glassed-in cabin, languishing from heat and boredom, four more half-dressed men lay sprawled about, each in the position most comfortable for him, now and then lazily exchanging words. On the walls of the cabin hung rifles, pistols and ammunition belts. On the floor were narrow metal boxes with machinegun belts, and boxes of ammunition. In one of the boxes were carelessly laid hand grenades, some bottle-shaped, and some lemon-shaped with grooves. Sacks of canned food and other products also lay about. On the benches discarded items of uniform lay scattered about in disorder. At the wheel, in the same half-dressed condition, with a pistol on a belt and with binoculars on his breast stood the helmsman, attentively straining his gaze into the distance along the hardly bending river. The banks were sloping, overgrown with thick underbrush, behind which stretched up rocky precipices, covering the horizon.

For two weeks already this crew of the "Kavasaki" had been patrolling along the Berelekh River. The vigilance of the first days had passed, and only the helmsman standing on watch continued to keep alert. Everybody was bored by the monotonous, fruitless and seemingly purposeless sailing the river in the *taiga* with its uninteresting, unpopulated wild banks. . . .

Suddenly the helmsman noticed something floating down the river toward the cutter. He shouted into the cabin, and at his call, lazily stretching himself, the commander of the crew came out. The musing machinegunner slowly roused himself a little, and also began to direct his gaze in the direction of the floating object. In the binoculars it was possible to make out three rafts, with people on them. A chance human encounter in the lonely *taiga*, after a long period of complete isolation from the outside world, introduced variety and was a welcome event for the crew. Everybody came out on deck, anticipating no danger, since during the last two weeks all hope of meeting with Gamailis' group had disappeared. The men of the crew eagerly and curiously waited for the cutter and the raft to approach each other more closely. In the binoculars it was already possible to make out people in military uniforms and with rifles. In the full belief that the raft carried soldiers of some search group, the crew of the cutter happily shouted to them, waving their hands.

It was soon noticed, however, that those on the rafts did not share in this joy at the prospect of meeting with the cutter. The rafts hastily began to make for the shore. This seemed suspicious. The cutter gave full speed. Already it was possible with the naked eye to see armed people leaping quickly from the rafts to the bank. All doubts vanished. The crew quickly readied their weapons and prepared for battle. The commander of the crew through his megaphone ordered the unidentified group to stand motionless on the bank. They paid no attention to him. The machinegun fired several short bursts into the air in the direction of the rafts. In reply shots were heard coming from the bank. It became evident that this was Gamailis' group. But why were there so many of them, why were they in military uniform? The details of Gamailis' activities during the last days were unknown to the crew of the cutter. They knew only what was in the initial reports, that the group of prisoners who had fled with Gamailis were only ten men in all.

The distance separating the raft and the cutter had narrowed to two hundred meters. From the shore the firing became more intense. From the cutter the machinegun went into action, spraying the shore with lead. From the shore a rapid firing continued. The bullets whistled over the heads of the crew; the cutter received several hits. The helmsman was wounded, but remained at the wheel. The cutter indecisively halted in the middle of the river. It was dangerous to come closer. The exchange of fire continued.

At this time several armed horsemen showed themselves from the underbrush in various places on the opposite bank of the river. When they saw what was going on, they concealed themselves again, but soon from that shore, exactly opposite Gamailis' people an intense rifle and machinegun fire opened up. This was a mounted search group which was passing by, and had been attracted by the firing on the river. It was possible to perceive by the tempo of the firing that confusion had developed in Gamailis' group, but they did not abandon their positions on the bank, and continued to return the fire. The machinegun on the cutter chattered, firing belt after belt. But then something fell in the water near the cutter, and immediately thereafter a dull underwater explosion occurred. A column of water shot up. Before the crew of the cutter could comprehend what was happening, another explosion was heard at the stern. Again and again the splashes of water from the falling grenades, the dull explosions, the watery fountains. The cutter went into reverse.

From the shore, not more than fifty meters from the cutter, shots were heard. The helmsman, pouring blood, slid down from the wheel, fell overboard, and gasping, thrashing his arms, crying for help, disappeared under the water.

The cutter went out of control, and continuing to go in reverse, began to approach the hostile shore. The commander of the crew jumped to the wheel, in order to replace the killed helmsman, but suddenly he too squirmed and fell over the wheel. A third took the wheel, and the cutter began to withdraw at full speed down the river from the scene of danger.

From the shore the soldiers continued intense fire on Gamailis' people. It was soon noticed, however, that they had ceased to return the fire. The firing gradually ceased and a deathly silence set in, but nobody as yet came out of cover.

The cutter had retired a few hundred meters down the river, and now began to discharge rockets into the air. After a while a few horsemen showed themselves on the bank. This turned out to be a new search group which had been attracted by the shooting. On the bank foot soldiers began to show themselves, at first cautiously, crouching and keeping to cover, and then more and more audaciously. Finally it was possible to count about thirty persons, mounted and on foot. They began to gather in groups, abandoning their caution, and in loud voices discussed what had taken place. Several were wounded; these were given first aid. The soldiers searched through the bushes with dogs, looking for killed and wounded. From one place and another they carried out the corpses of the soldiers, and carefully laid them in a row on the river bank. It turned out that there were eight soldiers killed in the exchange of fire. Three more were seriously wounded and could not get up. Inarticulate groans tore themselves from their breasts. They breathed heavily, wheezing. One soldier was seriously wounded in the abdomen. With a bloody foam in his mouth and hardly able to speak, he groaned, "Shoot, boys, finish me off . . . I can't stand it."

Everybody was tense and nervous. Their movements were erratic. Nobody paid any attention to the cries and groans of the dying. Ten mounted soldiers with five dogs crossed the river by swimming. Those who remained on the bank prepared themselves for battle in case of attack from the other side. Once again complete silence ensued, broken only by the lapping of the water and the snorting of the swimming horses.

The cutter came up and began to transport the foot soldiers to the other shore, while the mounted soldiers crossed on their swimming horses. The soldiers, upon coming out onto the other shore, set the dogs free in the underbrush and themselves moved after them, with slung rifles, overcoming the thickets with difficulty. The despairing barks of the dogs were heard first in one place, then in another. All the soldiers had already reached the other bank. From the bushes they carried out the dead of Gamailis' group. There were eight of them, just as there had been eight of the soldiers killed. One of the soldiers joked, "Well, how about that! It turned out to be a ruble for a ruble." An officer cut the joker short with the remark, "That counter-revolutionary scum isn't worth a broken half-kopeck!"

They also found wounded members of Gamailis' group. There were three of them. From an interrogation it was possible to establish that Gamailis had twenty-seven men. All the prisoners from Geological Party No. 8, upon which the attack had recently been made, had joined him. There could be no delay. Gamailis must be pursued, and not allowed to get too far away. As a result of the skirmish two hours had been lost already.

They buried the dead soldiers on the bank, but left the bodies of the prisoners in a heap, after having taken their fingerprints. The wounded soldiers and the three captured people of Gamailis were sent off on the cutter to Elik, to Yakubovsky's headquarters, together with a report of the encounter. The soldiers set off on the fresh trail of Gamailis.

VI

THE PRISONERS

The cutter went at full speed up the Berelekh River, from time to time giving out alarm whistles and releasing colored rockets. After about twenty kilometers they heard shots, and not far from the river they saw a rocket go up. The cutter halted, and continued to give signals. They also prepared themselves for battle. After a certain time horsemen showed themselves on the shore. This was still another search group, consisting of twenty soldiers with dogs. It was following the trail of Gamailis' pack horses, which had been discovered a few dozen meters from the river. This group was apprised of what had happened. The horsemen set off at a swift pace to the scene of the incident, hastening to capture the pack animals traveling with Gamailis' reserves, to prevent them from joining forces with him. The cutter continued on its way.

Not until the third day were the wounded soldiers and the captured men of Gamailis delivered at Yakubovsky's headquarters. Once again messengers were dispatched in all directions, and over the *taiga* flew airplanes, scattering pennants with orders. The prisoners were submitted to a careful interrogation. Yakubovsky himself questioned them.

One of them was an engineer of Geologic Party No. 54, who had fled together with Gamailis. The other two were prisoner workers from Geologic Party No. 8. The engineer was subjected to a particularly severe interrogation. He answered the questions curtly. He looked Yakubovsky in the eye courageously, and with hatred.

". . . I'll tell you the truth. Maybe what I say will reach your conscience. If not now, then perhaps some day. I don't intend to conceal anything. I'll even tell you things which under other circumstances could bring harm to my friends. But they're done for. There's no doubt about that. They're still alive today, maybe, but tomorrow, or the day after . . . they'll all be destroyed. There's no way out for us any more. None whatsoever. That's the way things turned out. I understand this very well—we all do. Gamailis knows, and so do we, that it's all over. We know that our luck has run out. We can't get away from you, and now we have to die. It's only a question of time. A matter of days—maybe only hours.

"Why did we run away? We wanted to feel a little joy, a last little chance to save our lives. 'Kolyma' is death. A slow one or a quick one, depending on how you look at it. On 'Kolyma' the quick death is the sweeter of the two.

"There was one prisoner among us, a former officer of the border troops, who had served on frontier duty on the shore of the Sea of Okhotsk. Two years ago he was sentenced to ten years for having failed to prevent two Japanese from crossing the border. He wasn't guilty, but he was charged with negligence. After the trial he tried to commit suicide. He didn't make it. And so he landed on 'Kolyma.' For almost ten years he had guarded the border on the shores of the Sea of Okhotsk. He knows very well how this sector is controlled. He knows the coastal fishing villages and the Japanese fishing concessions on these coasts. With his help we wanted to get hold of a fishing boat or a cutter, and make our way to the Kurile Islands. Maybe we would have met a foreign steamer on the way. We would have been saved. We were sure they wouldn't turn us in. They would have helped us, given us asylum. . . .

"On the fifth week of our wandering around in the *taiga*, when the first encounter with the soldiers of the guard occurred, we understood that our plan wouldn't work. They were all over us. We weren't able to avoid the search groups. We saw that death was waiting for us, but we wanted to sell our lives dearly. You won't get them cheap.

"You can't possibly understand how terrible, how hard it is to die off helplessly, in full realization of your complete powerlessness and the absolute inevitability of your doom. . . . And it's even more terrible to die at the hands of the executioners, with a bullet in the back of your head. . . . But the joy of dying in battle against your torturers, against the regime—yes, even in a battle that is doomed to failure—in a fight like this you try to sell your life as dearly as possible, right up to your last breath. . . . You fight. . . . We made this decision, together with Gamailis. We resolved to fight you to the last drop of our blood, to the last breath of our life. Death in battle—that was our motto.

"You can't understand this. I know what I'm saying doesn't satisfy you. I've said very little that you could put into the protocol of an interrogation and use for your purposes. But I'll tell you nothing more. You can't beat another word out of me."

The prisoner fell silent, breathing heavily, glaring with hatred at Yakubovsky. Yakubovsky, sitting on the stump of a felled tree, looked sullenly at the prisoner. It was evident that he was restraining himself to his utmost, and was pondering what he now had to do with his enemy. Complete silence prevailed for several seconds. None of the officers present uttered a word. The speech of the prisoner had by its courage and frankness produced a stunning effect on everyone present.

Suddenly the prisoner's eyes lit up. He continued, "When they captured me, your soldiers and I saw on the bank the bodies of my friends lying in a heap. I envied them. I envy Gamailis, and our friends who are still with him. They will have the pleasure of dying in the act of destroying you snakes, you depraved haters of mankind, you scum of our people. God damn you! Your children will be ashamed of their fathers. You. . . ."

Yakubovsky got up to his entire gigantic height and with a strong blow of his enormous fist struck the prisoner in the face, knocking him off his feet, and silencing him. The prisoner, sitting on the ground, covered his face with both hands. Blood trickled through his fingers in streams, running over his bare neck and over his wounded chest, bandaged with dirty rags.

"Get up and go over there!" Yakubovsky pointed in the direction of the bushes.

One of the officers present, turning to Yakubovsky, said, "I would like to interrogate the prisoner on some details which could have an important significance in connection with the operation."

Yakubovsky looked at him angrily and answered, "Interrogate the other two. They'll tell you more." And then, turning to the prisoner, angrily, "All right you, stand up and get moving."

The prisoner got up slowly and with difficulty and,

swaying, with an uncertain gait, hanging his head, started toward the bushes in the direction in which Yakubovsky was pointing.

Yakubovsky turned to the officers present with a grin. "Comrade Colt will have a talk with him now," he said, and followed after the prisoner. As he walked he drew his large-caliber Colt out of its holster.

From the bushes was heard the dry sound of the shot, and then a second, a third. . . .

And then Yakubovsky appeared in the clearing again. He was wiping his hands and his sweated brow with a handkerchief. Evidently desiring to dispel the unpleasant impression which had been produced on the officers, he said in a familiar tone, "I'm surprised at you, comrade officers. You seem to have rather strange concepts. There's a kind of decadent, chivalrous spirit which persists in you, a musty outmoded sentimentality, an unneeded gallantry. Remember this, that to destroy the enemy is the honor of the Chekist. But you—you see as enemies only those who stand before you with weapons in their hands. And once they are disarmed, you become limp. We would have betrayed the Revolution long ago, had we listened to such concepts. Remember what Comrade Lenin and Comrade Stalin teach us: if the enemy does not surrender, he must be destroyed!"

The two remaining prisoners were interrogated. One of them was trembling from fear during the questioning, as if in ague. His lower jaw drew up convulsively. With tears in his eyes he looked at Yakubovsky and the others in supplication. He talked rapidly and eagerly, and too much. He told them all they wanted to know, in complete detail. He was trying to redeem himself, he blamed everything on his comrades, on Gamailis. He talked about the compulsion and the threats which Gamailis had used on him, and about how he had wanted to leave Gamailis immediately and tell everything to the guards, but was waiting only for the proper moment. He tried to exculpate himself in a base and cowardly manner. He wept; he begged for mercy on his knees. He promised to do anything and everything demanded of him in order to redeem himself. . . . And in a whisper, with frequent nervous side-glances, he proposed that he be returned to Gamailis, in order to provide information concerning his activities. He evoked no sympathy or pity whatsoever by his conduct. Even Yakubovsky expressed his disdain for him. "You're a fine one. Now you want to sell out your friends. You should have thought of it sooner. It's a little late now. You'll get what's good for you. In the next world you'll meet up with Gamailis. He'll give you some more."

The other one was sullen, indifferent, taciturn. He avoided direct answers, and spoke quietly, in a detached manner, unwillingly. Outwardly he seemed completely detached. During the interrogation he frequently adjusted the bandage on his wounded leg, which was bare above the knee. Now and then he squeezed it, his face distorted in pain. In reply to one of Yakubovsky's questions he said, as if he had not heard him, "Could I have a clean bandage to bind the leg? It hurts so, I can hardly stand it."

Yakubovsky answered him with a grin, "Bear up a little longer. Pretty soon it will be over and you won't need a bandage."

"Well, all right, I'll try to make out with it. There's nothing else to do, seeing how things are," he said in a very quiet voice, as if regretting only that they had refused him a bandage. Then he looked quickly at Yakubovsky with hatred, and added, "Get it over with quick, you skunk.

There's nothing more to talk about." At the conclusion of each interrogation Yakubovsky led his victims off into the bushes to "have a talk with Comrade Colt."

Early on the morning of the next day Yakubovsky and his staff took off on horses in the direction of Gamailis' location. On the following day, toward evening, they reached the Berelekh River, boarded a cutter, and after a few hours were already on the scene of the recent battle with Gamailis. Upon arrival in the area, Yakubovsky learned that Gamailis had fled with his men into the mountains after the battle. He set out in pursuit, and followed the trail right up to the base of the mountains. It was impossible to proceed further because of oncoming darkness, the difficult, rocky terrain, and the inadequate number of search groups available at the moment.

Additional search groups kept arriving from various directions. They deployed at the base of the mountains. Gamailis' pack horses had been captured with the five of his men who were leading them. During the capture they had offered no resistance. Yakubovsky interrogated them, and then they were disposed of in the same manner as the other three prisoners had been.

Airplanes continued to hover over the mountainous mass in which Gamailis had taken refuge, releasing colored rockets, pinpointing his location.

VII

GAMAILIS' END

For three days and nights the search groups had been climbing about in the rocky, sparsely vegetated mountains, covering the ground with difficulty, narrowing the circle around Gamailis. In the mountains distance is deceptive, and it is more difficult to gauge than on level ground. You look at some near-lying prominence of mountain and it seems quite close, not more than a kilometer away, as the crow flies, but when you set off toward it, you need almost a whole day to get there. Up, down, up again, orienting yourself on prominent features of the cliffs, you cover the distance slowly, and you gradually develop the impression that as you move forward the goal keeps receding, and you feel that you will never get there. It's not easy to cover distance in the mountains.

The soldiers frequently lost their footing and tumbled down the slopes, injuring themselves on the rocks. They were obliged to move over ground on which no human being had ever set foot before. They were suffering from the heat and the fatigue, the short rations, of which each man had to carry several days' supply on his own back. The water which they were carrying in their canteens was to last for several days, unless by chance they were so fortunate as to meet a spring along the way. The rifles, full cartridge belts, and the hand grenades further impeded their movement. Gamailis was showing no sign of himself, and if it had not been for the airplanes and their flares, showing where they had spotted him, it would have seemed as if he had already slipped through the encirclement, and that he was nowhere in the mountains.

And then, along toward the failing of daylight, it was possible to make out moving points in the distance on the slopes of the mountain, in the shadows between the rocks. Only with difficulty, with binoculars, was it possible to make out the armed men. No answer was received to the pre-arranged recognition signal provided for such an incident. The search group started toward the place, but was met by rifle fire.

The fire attracted the attention of the other search groups which were located in the area. The soldiers hastened to the scene of the firing, surrounding Gamailis and his men. Gamailis' men, upon disengaging themselves from the one search group with which they had been exchanging fire, suddenly met fire from another direction. Avoiding engagement, and merely answering with a few shots, they drew to one flank, but here too, they ran into an ambush which opened fire on them. Gamailis' men hurled themselves, like beasts at bay, from one rocky height to another, but wherever they turned they were met by fire from yet another group of soldiers. Through the mountains on all sides rang the shouts of people, commands, the barking of dogs, shots, and every now and then the flare of rockets.

Several of Gamailis' men had already been killed. He was forced to break out under cover of dark to conceal himself. Night called a halt to the action. Under darkness the situation became more complicated for Gamailis. He was hemmed in on all sides, in a small rocky region. In the morning a desperate last skirmish faced him, one which must cost many of their lives. No one had any doubt that Gamailis and his men would under no circumstances give themselves up, that they would sell their lives dearly.

Gamailis must surely have realized the hopelessness of his situation. He could not fail to see the soaring rockets which were sent up the whole night long. The rockets were shooting up from all sides of the place where Gamailis, with the remainder of his people, was spending his last night, waiting for the dawn. There was no way out for them. With the dawn they must meet their fate.

The search groups disposed themselves for the night, and put out sentries. Everybody was happy over the prospect of an early conclusion to the exhausting and dangerous operation, but not for a minute were they left without anxiety over the coming day. Everyone understood that with the dawn a meeting face to face with death was waiting for him. Who would be spared? The influence of the night, and the silence of the wild mountains further affected the mood and intensified the impressionability of the exhausted soldiers. They lay down to sleep in twos and threes together, keeping their weapons by their sides. They were pensive, yet tried to conceal their anxiety. Quietly, in whispers, they talked among themselves.

"Yesterday Yakubovsky comes up to me in a good mood and says, 'Well, what do you say, Semeonov, tomorrow we'll have a scrap and catch Gamailis?' So I tell him, 'We'll have a scrap all right, and maybe we'll catch him–maybe you'll show us how!' "

Another voice was heard from the darkness, "He'll get you for that crack. You'll find out how you have to talk to Yakubovsky."

"So what can he do to me? I do my job; my commander's satisfied with me. What does Yakubovsky have to do with me? We're the ones who do the fighting, and we're the ones who'll catch him. How much fighting has Yakubovsky seen? How many has he caught? I don't mind telling you, I'm not exactly sick with love for these Chekists."

"That's all very fine, but just the same, they're in the driver's seat. They don't even consult with our commanders. Just today, when I was on messenger detail, I took a report to headquarters, delivered a package. I hung around outside Yakubovsky's tent to rest up a bit. Inside I hear Yakubovsky talking with our officers. One of them is talking about how many of our soldiers have died because of Gamailis. 'Thirty men killed so far,' he says, 'and after tomorrow maybe just as many more. What for,' he says, 'why was this operation necessary? Where is Gamailis going to get to, how's he going to get out of the *taiga*? Where can he go? And if he gets out to Yakutsk or to the coast, then we could catch him there with our bare hands, and you wouldn't have to kill all these men. . . .' "

"And he's right, too. It makes sense. He's a reasonable man."

"Yeah, he's reasonable. He's understanding. And what do you think Yakubovsky said to him? He started to shout at him, 'Who do you think you are to question Berzin's orders! Do you want to go before a court?' I'll tell you, friend, that officer put his tail between his legs right quick. 'I'm not questioning the order,' he says. 'It's quite alright with me. Don't get me wrong. I was only thinking. . . .' So he's reasonable. So he's right. So where did it get him? I'll tell you how things are around here. Yakubovsky's running the whole show. He can even shoot you, if he wants to."

"That's a lot of baloney. Nobody has the right to shoot you if you didn't do anything. No court would stand behind it. You're running off at the mouth, friend."

"Oh no, you're the stupid one. You don't listen to anything but what the propagandists tell us, and what's written in the political booklets. Don't you ever think for yourself? Listen, mister, I know what the score is. Look at Rozanov. They shot him for nothing. Why? Simply because Berzin had to have it that way, that's why! That's the way things are. Can't you understand that? Berzin ordered the court to sentence execution, and the court sentenced it. Yakubovsky did the shooting himself."

"Who's Rozanov?"

"Who's Rozanov? Why, our soldier from the Seimchan battalion, who was guarding Gamailis and the others in the *taiga*. When they killed all the soldiers, Rozanov and the engineer Petrov were the ones who ran away and came to the camp and told what had happened. First they arrested them, and then they shot them. And what for? He did his duty too, just like you, and they took him out and shot him. Look out they don't arrest you, if you don't catch Gamailis. Berzin said so–if you don't catch him, you go before a court. Yakubovsky said so himself. I heard it."

"No, there's something not right here. It can't be that way. I can't believe it. Why should they arrest us if we don't catch Gamailis? We have nothing to do with the way it comes out. And you want me to believe that if we don't get him, we'll have to run off into the *taiga* ourselves, so they can't shoot us?"

"And where will you run to, in the *taiga*?" said another voice. "You won't get anywhere. And if you do get away, they'll grab your wife, your brother, your father. They'll take it out on them. And when they catch you, brother, look out! Now take Gamailis. Don't compare yourself with him, but he ran away, and you can see for yourself what happened. Better see to it, brother, that everything goes just as it should, like the bosses want it. If something doesn't go off quite right, then it's your neck. Don't forget it."

"Yeah, it's a tough job we have. You can't be happy in it."

"And do you think we're the only ones who have it like this? It's the same all over. Take the kolkhozes, for example. How do they live there? Take my father for example. . . ."

The soldiers talked among themselves for a long time in the dark, exchanging their recollections and thoughts. They did not notice that silently, under cover of darkness, a shadow came up to first one group, then another, standing in the gloom, listening to the conversations.

Gradually the talking came to an end, and the soldiers fell into a deep sleep. At last everything was quiet, and only the sentries could be heard going about the bivouacs, fighting their fatigue, fending off sleep.

With the dawn the firing started up again. At first single shots boomed about hollowly in the mountains, and then the shots increased in frequency and became a continuous crackle. Then once again it would become quiet. Then, after a short lull, gunfire would suddenly roll out again with full strength. Somewhere in the heights could be heard the furious barking and snarling of the dogs.

Gamailis' men had dispersed themselves in the rocky heights, and making use of cover, returned the fire and withdrew in various directions from the soldiers pursuing them. The soldiers, who were literally obliged to besiege each defender who had hidden himself among the rocks, sustained large losses. The attack on each fugitive was continued until he had been killed, or until he ran out of ammunition. Each man of Gamailis killed cost the lives of several soldiers. Those whom the soldiers could not reach with bullets, they showered with grenades, and turned the dogs loose on them. The dogs, unnoticed, noiselessly made their way between the rocks and unexpectedly leaped upon the defenders from behind, or from one side, lunging, frenziedly snapping their jaws.

In some places there was hand-to-hand combat. Having expended all their ammunition, Gamailis' men desperately threw themselves on the soldiers in the hope of destroying, before their death, at least one more hated enemy. In these moments the soldiers became symbols of the hated regime which had tortured them for many years. The hour had come to repay all the insults, the suffering which the system had heaped upon them for so long. With savage joy they avenged themselves, their loved ones, their relatives, their people. They were paying everything back now, here in the wild mountains against these common soldiers, who were compelled by the force of long service, of cruel discipline, to die by tens in order to destroy one.

Here one stubbornly returned fire from behind good rocky cover. Ten, fifteen soldiers lay fire on him. Whining bullets fly about him; chips of stone fly off the rocks with a crackle. Here one soldier, there another, hit by the bullets, comes to rest with his face downward, and lies motionless.

Here one of the defenders runs out of ammunition. He jumps up. His face is white and panic-stricken, his clothing smeared with blood. Holding his rifle with both hands by the barrel, he runs down the slope, hoping to strike a last blow with the stock. He is struck down by bullets; he falls, and slides downward. The soldiers get up and run to the assistance of their comrades who are still fighting.

Here one defender suddenly gets up on his feet from behind a rock and, paying no attention to the shots directed at him, throws away his rifle and raises his hands. The soldiers hold their fire, call him to approach. He comes nearer, not lowering his raised hands. His face is overgrown with a beard, and he is covered with dirt and blood. He is quite close now. Suddenly, with a quick movement he brings out an axe from behind his back and, making a swing with it at the head of a soldier, he falls, hit by bullets, without having succeeded in delivering the blow.

Here, after a protracted exchange of fire, a defender stops shooting. He lies behind a stone motionless. The soldiers run off to take on other defenders. The one lying motionless suddenly springs up and grabs a soldier by his belt, and with him throws himself upon another, knocking him from his feet. All three fall off the precipice, to be crushed on the rocks below.

Gamailis' people in their desperation were showing a miraculous heroism. Their fear of what would happen to them in the event of their capture was stronger than their fear of death. The soldiers looked in vain among the dead for Gamailis. He was not to be found. The fighting was drawing to a close. Only in a few places was firing still in progress. Already on the slope the soldiers were walking about freely with the dogs, collecting the killed and wounded. On every side Gamailis' name was spoken. But he could not be found.

Then somebody noticed at a distance of a few dozen meters the figure of a man clambering on a sharp promontory up above. The officers turned their binoculars on him. "Gamailis!" somebody shouted, and everybody, without command, impelled by one instinct, broke into a run, with rifles at the port, in the direction of the clambering figure. The dogs were turned loose and, leaving the soldiers far behind, they took off with excited barks in that direction, nimbly threading their way upward through the rocks, overtaking Gamailis.

Shots were heard from behind the rocks. The wounded dogs, yelping with pain, rolled down the rocks, one after the other. Intense fire was opened on Gamailis. He did not reply, and he did not show himself from behind his cover. But whenever the firing lulled, he hit one soldier here, another there, with well-aimed shots. Showering the rocky mass behind which Gamailis was concealed with a hail of bullets, the soldiers moved forward toward him. He threw two hand grenades down on them. He occupied a very advantageous position on a cliff, and was covered from all sides. The soldiers, on the other hand, were obliged to move upwards from below, exposing themselves to his fire. Hand grenades were hurled at Gamailis; they exploded without reaching him. Then finally, one well-thrown grenade flew over Gamailis' refuge and exploded right on his position.

Everybody stood still, their eyes riveted to the place where the grenade had exploded. A few minutes passed in complete silence. The soldiers got up and began to clamber upwards. There remained a few paces to Gamailis' cover. The soldiers stopped, they were reluctant to come closer. They threw a few grenades, released the dogs. After this they came closer and behind the rock cover they saw a prone body, so mutilated by the grenades that it was beyond recognition. The dogs strained upward; it was barely possible to hold them back on their leashes. The soldiers crowded around the body. Nobody doubted that it was Gamailis.

Every man congratulated one another.

Unexpectedly, from above, a grenade fell into the crowd of soldiers and lay hissing on the ground. Somebody quickly seized it, to throw it off to one side, but at that moment it exploded. Those soldiers who were unharmed tried to dash away, but they were on a small platform of rock, from which it was not easy to disperse. There was hardly any cover. Another grenade fell and exploded, and from above firing began, hitting the soldiers who had hastily sought out promontories of rock as cover. The soldiers did not return the fire; they sought only to save themselves. On the spot of the explosions there remained many killed and wounded.

From down below intense fire was opened on the man who was concealed in the rocks. He returned it. Fate was preserving him. He seemed to have firmly decided not to die as long as he had any ammunition with which to resist. It was decided to go around the mountain and take him from above. Twilight was coming on.

Going around from behind, and coming out above the defender's position, the soldiers saw Gamailis below them, several meters away, sitting on a small platform of rock, binding his wounds. His rifle and several grenades lay nearby. There were full ammunition belts, and on another belt hung a pistol.

A shot was fired and Gamailis, hit, writhing like a snake, crawled off behind a rock, dragging his rifle with him, but leaving the ammunition belt where it was. The soldiers began to climb down to him, but when they had reached the place, Gamailis was already not there. A bloody trail stretched off among the rocks, and the soldiers began to move cautiously forward in this direction. Between the rocks they saw the discarded rifle, and not far off, Gamailis lay stretched out, flowing blood. With great difficulty he raised his pistol with both hands and fired two shots. They missed. A salvo from several rifles was fired almost point-blank at the dying man.

At last silence reigned in the mountains once again. On

the scene of the fight they buried the dead soldiers. Gamailis' captured men were interrogated, and in the silence, from time to time, there rang out the dry shots of Yakubovsky's Colt.

An airplane flew over the *taiga*, with its course set for Magadan, carrying the report to Berzin, "Mission accomplished–escape of Gamailis unsuccessful."

SVIRKO

THE name Svirko should be very well known to anyone who was on "Kolyma" in the 1930's. He was a young Soviet engineer and geologist who, after completing his training at the institute in Moscow in 1932, went to "Kolyma" as a volunteer to work in his profession. He had no family, no close friends, he lived alone, and on "Kolyma" the pay was good. Svirko went after the "long ruble," as the saying goes. He didn't work long as a geologist however. His sharp wits soon whispered to him that on "Kolyma" one could work less, get more and live better. Svirko soon accustomed himself to the atmosphere of the Soviet concentration camps. He quickly learned the nature and the tastes of the mighty Chekist Berzin, unlimited ruler of "Kolyma," a favorite of Stalin himself. Svirko managed to get close to Berzin, to please him and to make a favorable impression on him. Very soon after his arrival on "Kolyma" Svirko was made chief of the Urutukan division of the camp, located in the wild, silent *taiga*, three hundred and fifty kilometers from the administrative center at Magadan. He had fifty to sixty thousand prisoners at his complete disposal. With these forces he mined gold, and built the road which was to cut through the loneliness of the *taiga* for thousands of kilometers in the direction of Yakutsk.

Tempo! Tempo! Tempo! Fulfill the production and construction plans at all cost! Over-fulfill the plans! Disregard the cost, even if it be the lives of thousands of prisoner-slaves. Raise the norms! Raise them again! And so on, without end. The men, the slaves perished from labor beyond their strength, from malnutrition, from the cold, but the plans were fulfilled. The building of socialism marched on at full speed. Communism triumphed.

To replace those who perished in the *taiga* ever newer and newer thousands of prisoners were sent to Svirko. So far as the supply of worker forces were concerned, there was no problem. "Our human resources are unlimited," Stalin had said. His words were fully confirmed on "Kolyma." Svirko quickly assumed the role of lord and master of all. In the course of two years he achieved for himself a magnificent production record, and what was even more important, Berzin's favor. He enjoyed Berzin's complete confidence, became his darling. In Berzin's support lay Svirko's enormous power.

Svirko accustomed himself, not only to the role of administrator, but also to that of grand inquisitor over the prisoners. The passion of the sadist, latent in his nature, appeared suddenly in the strongest degree. He was a cruel and cunning beast. In justification of his conduct, he liked to refer to himself as a Chekist. "We Chekists," he would say, "must stop at nothing in the building of Communism! We must be merciless in the process of erecting our Communist state, and in the strengthening of our great Party!"

Torturing human beings was a necessity of life for Svirko, and he did it with passion, with irrepressible delight. Berzin forgave him everything he did out there in the *taiga*. Or perhaps it would be more proper to say that he simply paid no attention to anything Svirko did, except his successful fulfillment of the production plans.

Many of the prisoners committed to Svirko's charge experienced the terrible exquisiteness of his passion. He liked to interrogate personally those who might be guilty of infractions of the camp rules, although this was completely outside the purview of his responsibilities, since he had a special operative-Chekist department in his organization for this purpose. For the prisoners Svirko's tormenting interrogations were more dreaded than those of the professional Chekists who, as everyone knows, are not particularly known for their gentleness. Frequently, when prisoners were stubborn at interrogations and would not confess, the Chekist interrogators would frighten them with the threat that Svirko himself would call them up for a personal interview. Such a threat would be sufficient to make the prisoners tell all they knew, and furthermore, when the interrogators demanded it, to take upon themselves the blame for deeds which they had never committed, and concerning which they had not the slightest knowledge. All the consequences which could arise as a result of such confessions—trial by court, increase of prison term, and even the firing squad—were less terrible for them than the prospect of ending up at an interrogation with the chief of the camp division, that enthusiast of socialist construction, that engineer-geologist, young Communist Party member and amateur-Chekist, Svirko.

Usually Svirko questioned prisoners alone, behind closed doors, in the office which he had in his large bachelor apartment. After these interrogations the prisoners would be led out or carried out on stretchers, bloody, crippled, often with broken bones and knocked out teeth. During these interrogations shrieks could be heard from Svirko's house, and groans, the sound of falling bodies, and shots. He did not kill his victims at interrogations, but sometimes for its terrorizing effect he would fire pistol shots over the head of the person being questioned, or would shoot non-vital parts of the body. When he felt stronger measures to be necessary, he would plunge a knife, a fork or some other sharp instrument into the body of his victim. He would beat prisoners in the face with his fist, with a stick, or with a lash. Into the open wounds he would throw a handful of salt. He would rage and storm and then, right in the midst of this, would go over into a mood of happy exhilaration.

Svirko liked to drench a prisoner with water and then take him outside where the temperature was forty degrees below zero, and force him to walk around. He himself would dress in a warm fox fur coat, a furry squirrel cap, buckskin boots with fur above the knee and warm gloves and would walk along beside his victim until the latter was no longer able to move in his frozen clothing. Then Svirko would stop, light up a cigarette and stand looking at this living ice-block, laughing at the poor wretch's misery. At such times he would like to display his curiosity in a joking manner. "Well, how are you now, my dear fellow? Cold?" he would ask. "Why are you standing still? Move about! Get warm! Tell me, how do you feel now?" He would say all this slowly, with a quiet, sympathetic tone of voice, with a nuance of derision. When this bored him, he would order the frozen man to be carried into his office, and the interrogation would continue.

After each interrogation Svirko would call a recess until the following evening. During this recess the prisoner would be put back in the cement-walled cold-cell of the prison, where he would usually fall on the floor in a state of exhaustion. Many did not survive these recesses, and died in the cell. They were written off the books as having died of "natural causes." Nobody concerned himself as to the cause of their death.

Svirko acquired fame as a pitiless, bloodthirsty beast. The mention of his name was enough to bring terror to the prisoners. His own administrative organization trembled before him. The soldiers and officers of the guard also feared him. Everybody knew that he was Berzin's favorite, which was the same as saying, all-powerful. Such a man was Svirko.

In this manner Svirko, establishing an arbitrary regime, passed himself off with complete impunity as a true and devoted son of the Party, a Chekist irreconcilably ruthless toward its enemies, an organizer and a leader. He founded for himself on "Kolyma" a new career, and set his eyes on the "brilliant Future," counting on Berzin's continued favor.

* * *

In the Urutukan division of the camp, where Svirko was in charge, there was among the prisoners a former Soviet engineer by the name of Voskoboinikov, who had been sentenced for counter-revolutionary activity. For some reason not clear, Svirko had accused Voskoboinikov of having engaged in sabotage, of having obstructed the production plans, and of having incited a rebellion of the prisoners against the camp discipline, against the administration, and against Svirko himself. He accused Voskoboinikov of having plotted a revolt of the prisoners. He ordered him arrested. When the inquiry had been concluded, the charge against Voskoboinikov was naturally sustained, since Svirko had ordered that he be proven guilty. The Voskoboinikov case was supposed to be sent to the camp center at Magadan for review at a special session of the judicial.

Svirko, upon acquainting himself with the results of the inquiry, was still not satisfied. Voskoboinikov's sabotage had been established conclusively, as well as agitation against the camp administration, but not one word had been said about the plotting of a revolt by the prisoners. Svirko wanted to make the matter reflect that he in his endeavors on behalf of the Party was constantly subject to danger from the prisoners, that plots were being organized against him, and that he through his diligence alone had averted a revolt. In short, it was the time-worn ruse for gaining recognition for the local command in the eyes of the high organs of state security, as well as commendations and, perhaps, decorations. Svirko decided to make good the "oversight" of the Chekist-investigator. He ordered that Voskoboinikov be brought to him for a personal interrogation.

During the course of three nights in a row, Svirko interrogated Voskoboinikov in his apartment, beating the necessary confessions out of him. Voskoboinikov was left without teeth as a result of this interrogation; one eye was beaten out of his head. His collar bone was broken, and several ribs. In due course Voskoboinikov, covered with wounds, confessed to everything demanded of him and, to Svirko's complete satisfaction, signed all the necessary protocols. After this Voskoboinikov was put back into his solitary confinement cell, and the results of the inquiry was sent off to Magadan. It was expected, naturally, that he would be sentenced to execution.

Svirko wrote a personal letter to Berzin, in which he described in detail all the difficulties and dangers which attended his post. After a few days an order came from Berzin that Voskoboinikov be delivered immediately to central headquarters in Magadan. The case was interesting to Berzin. He wanted to inflate the affair even further, in order to extract from it some personal benefit in his own report to Moscow. Berzin's request had to be fulfilled, but how? The fact of the matter was, there had been no conspiracy to revolt whatsoever; Voskoboinikov had made absolutely no attempt to assassinate Svirko. This could be embarrassing, if it were to become known in Magadan. Furthermore, how could the beaten, half-dead Voskoboinikov, with his broken bones, be delivered to Magadan for all to see?

That evening Svirko personally gave detailed instructions to the senior soldier of the escort guard, one Smirnov, in his private office. The next day, early in the morning, the mutilated and half-alive Voskoboinikov, wrapped up in a reindeer fur, was loaded into a sleigh pulled by two small shaggy Siberian horses. Alongside him rode two mounted guards, wrapped up in sheep furs. The party set off on the long road to Magadan.

A day passed, and a night, and another day. At evening of the second day, when it was already dark, the guard party which had set out on the day before returned to the hamlet of Urutukan. On the sleigh still lay Voskoboinikov, wrapped in the furs, just as on the morning before. He was dead. The soldiers left the horses on the edge of the village. Senior guard Smirnov set off in the direction of Svirko's house. They buried Voskoboinikov the same day. The guards had the following story to relate concerning what had happened.

Toward evening of the first day they decided to pass the night in the first house they might find along the way. It was already getting toward evening, when they came upon a small house standing by itself. They stopped, and both of the soldiers went in, to see what arrangements for sleeping could be made. They left Voskoboinikov in the sleigh. In a few minutes soldier Smirnov came out of the house, but the sleigh and Voskoboinikov were no longer there. Then, in the distance, he saw Voskoboinikov standing up in the sleigh, speeding down the road, urging on the horses, trying to escape. Soldier Smirnov began to shout, and to fire at the fleeing man. One of the shots hit him. The horses ran into a snowdrift and stopped. The other soldier ran out of the house at the sound of the shouts and the shooting. He saw only that the horses were standing in the snowdrift, and several paces away, lying stretched out on the road, lay Voskoboinikov, dead. Near him was standing soldier Smirnov. The soldiers picked up the dead man and started back to Urutukan. This was what the soldiers had to say about what had happened.

Svirko sent a report to Berzin, and after describing in detail what had happened along the road, made the following conclusion: "The escort guard was obliged to resort to arms in order to frustrate Voskoboinikov's attempt to escape. This measure was fully justified by the circumstances."

At the same time, through routine channels, he sent a report to Magadan to the commander of the operative-Chekist organization which had conducted the inquiry. Here also he made the conclusion that the use of firearms was "fully justified by the circumstances."

The chief of the operative-Chekist unit could not help but know in what condition Voskoboinikov had been when he was bundled off from Urutukan on the road to Magadan. He was an experienced Chekist however, and knew what attitude was required by the circumstances. He closed his eyes to certain things which it was not good for him to see.

The commander of the local unit of the guard also could not help but know about all this. He was an officer still inexperienced in the conditions of concentration camp life however, and did not yet possess sufficient seasoning, was not yet properly educated in the facts of life in Berzin's "Kolyma." He could not understand how the half-dead Voskoboinikov, wounded and with many broken bones, could have possibly attempted to escape. There was surely more here than met the eye; of this the commander had no doubt whatsoever. But why then, did soldier Smirnov shoot him? Why did the two soldiers corroborate each other in the fantastic tale that Voskoboinikov had been killed in an attempt to escape? The commander was lost in conjecture. He was completely unable to understand the matter.

He called in both of the soldiers and began to question them concerning details. The junior soldier was only able to relate what he had already said previously: "When I heard the shots I ran out of the house and saw . . ."

Soldier Smirnov repeated what he had already said several times before. The commander's doubt increased and, closeting himself with Smirnov alone, he posed severe and pointed questions to him.

"Did you shoot Voskoboinikov?"

"Yes, during an attempt to escape."

"How could Voskoboinikov attempt to escape, when he was barely alive?"

"I don't know how he did it, but he tried to escape."

"You're hiding something! Voskoboinikov couldn't have escaped. I know very well, and you know very well what condition Voskoboinikov was in. Tell me how it happened! If you lie to me any more I'll have you arrested and sent to headquarters in Magadan. There they'll interrogate you good and proper. I want the whole truth, and I want it right now!"

Soldier Smirnov lost his head, began to contradict his previous explanations, tried to disentangle himself, but he still avoided the truth. He finally became completely confused in his contradictions. At last he said in a dogged tone, "It was the way I said in the first place. I don't know anything more! Voskoboinikov tried to escape and I shot him."

When soldier Smirnov left the commander it was completely dark. After he left the *kaserne* he carefully, stealthily headed for Svirko's house, trying to avoid attracting attention.

After his conversation with Smirnov the commander remained convinced that the soldier had intentionally killed Voskoboinikov. He was indignant. In his inexperience and naïveté he began to write a report to the commander of the camp guard forces in Magadan, in which he explained everything he knew about the case, omitting no details.

Svirko's report and that of the commander of the guard

unit went to Magadan by the same express military courier, and only those who had written them knew of their contents.

On the next day Svirko summoned the commander of the guard unit and suggested pointedly to him that it would be well to terminate his investigation of the Voskoboinikov incident, and take no further measures. Life in the *taiga* continued on its way. Nobody spoke of what had happened. But the reports had been sent off, and they had been received in Magadan. Berzin, upon reading Svirko's report, directed that the matter be dropped. However, the commander of the guard forces in Magadan, not yet knowing Berzin's decision on this question, ordered that both soldiers be arrested and immediately delivered in Magadan to the guard forces headquarters.

When Svirko found out that the two soldiers had been arrested and sent off to Magadan, he was furious. "Who dared to do this without me? Bring them back!" he stormed. "Bring them back! Immediately!" But it was already too late. The two soldiers were already under guard and on their way to Magadan in a truck that was going that way. Regardless of the late hour, the agitated Svirko ordered that an automobile be brought up. He set off for Magadan.

The commander of the guard, not without reason, became uneasy, and being unable to stand the suspense, decided also to ride to central headquarters. Not having an automobile at his disposal, he ordered horses to be brought up, and without losing time also rode off to Magadan, hoping along the way to get a ride with some passing automobile.

The next morning Svirko was already closeted with Berzin in his office. Meanwhile the commander of the guard unit from Urutukan, muffled up in his sheepskin coat, burning with impatience and vexation, slowly dragged along the road. He did not meet a single automobile along the way. The chief of the guard forces meanwhile was personally interrogating the soldier Smirnov in his headquarters, in the presence of a commissar.

* * *

Smirnov was terrified by the unexpected turn of events. He could not know that the highest authorities had caused his arrest and ordered him brought to the center. He imagined everything, right up to the very worst, that could be in store for him. But the main thing that made him uneasy was that he found himself without the supporting presence of his protector Svirko. Morally he was already prepared for complete capitulation before the high-ranking officers who were questioning him.

"Well now, tell us what happened with you and Voskoboinikov," began the commander of the guard forces.

Soldier Smirnov was silent. He looked uneasily, first at the commander, and then at the commissar, hoping somehow from their faces to understand how much they knew of what had actually happened. Lowering his eyes, he became reflective, and after a long silence, he began, timidly, stumbling over his words.

"Well you see, Comrade Commander, it was a bad business. I understand that. But I really don't know—what can I do? It was a clumsy business. I know I can't get off without a trial. Anyway, how can I prove my innocence now? They interrogated me in Urutukan, they put together a protocol. I signed it, and now I have to say something absolutely different. Now you want the real truth from me.

"I lost my head completely, Comrade Commander; I was confused. I'll tell you the truth. I'll tell you how it was, but I beg you to help me. Tell me what I should do. Stand behind me. I give you my word, I won't hide anything from you—but save me! Who else can I turn to, except you?"

Smirnov hung his head and, covering his face with his hands, sat for a long time like this, silent and motionless.

The commander of the guard forces looked at his commissar significantly. The commissar nodded his head. This was more like it.

Presently Smirnov began again, in a quiet, timid voice, "Our chief Svirko noticed me a long time ago, and he always set me apart from the other soldiers. I don't know why, but I seemed to please him. Possibly because of my size, my strength. Whenever he met me he would always smile at me and he never passed by without saying something nice, or maybe a joke. Sometimes he would stop, give me a cigarette, and ask me, 'Well, what do you say, Big Boy, how's the world treating you?' When he needed a soldier to guard somebody he always called for me on the telephone. If I was on duty when he called, he would get mad and say, 'Well, then send me any knucklehead you've got there.' He didn't like the guards much, but he was always good to me.

"When he was interrogating Voskoboinikov he called for me. One time he even ordered me to be taken off charge of quarters duty. I sat at his place for three nights out in the corridor while he was interrogating Voskoboinikov. From outside the door I heard Svirko beating him, and Voskoboinikov groaning and sometimes screaming. The last night I almost passed out. He stripped him, and then began to jab him with a stick that had a sharp metal point. I could hear it all from the talk that came through the door. I went up to the door and began to look through the keyhole. There I see Svirko jabbing him with the sharp end of the stick. Voskoboinikov is covering his face with his hands, blood is flowing, but he's taking it, just groaning a little, and then suddenly he falls on the floor, and Svirko starts jabbing him as hard as he can, in the face, in the chest, in the belly. . . .

"I couldn't look any more. I sat down on the floor by the door. I began to feel queer, started to throw up. I wanted to run away, but I was afraid. After a while Svirko calls me into his office. On the floor there is Voskoboinikov, all in wounds, running with blood. He's lying there not moving. He's breathing hard, and just moves his lips, and blood is coming out of his mouth. Svirko tells me, 'Take this filthy thing and throw it in my cell,'—he has his own solitary cell in the prison—'and then come back here.'

"I took Voskoboinikov and hoisted him up on my shoulders. Svirko covered him with a canvas, and I carried him off in the dark to the prison. On sentry duty at the prison was the same soldier who later rode with me when we started off with Voskoboinikov. He's a young kid. I told him, 'Keep your mouth shut, and you won't get in trouble. You didn't see who I brought, and you don't know anything.' He was scared, but he got the idea. He's no fool.

"I went back to Svirko and he had me clean the floor. I cleaned it, straightened things up. Then he poured me a glass of vodka, gave me a cigarette, and began to tell me about how you have to handle enemies and counter-revolutionaries. Then he asked me who saw me carrying Voskoboinikov. I told him, only the soldier on sentry duty. Svirko gave me two bottles of vodka and some conserves, cigarettes, and told me, 'Divide it up with him, and tell him to keep his mouth shut. And as for you, don't you be foolish either. Play straight with me and you won't get into trouble. I'll always stand behind you. I'm a friend of Berzin himself. In Moscow the People's Commissar himself knows me. I can put you on a good road. . . . But if you start to flap your tongue, you'll have only yourself to blame. It will go hard with you!'

"After a few days Svirko called me in again. Offered me vodka, gave me a cigarette, and says to me, 'Tomorrow you'll take Voskoboinikov to Magadan, but he'll try to escape. Watch him carefully. If he runs, shoot! You'll be on the road for a week. It's a long road, and it's *taiga* all the way. If Voskoboinikov escapes, you'll wind up before a court yourself. I know that he'll try to escape. They're going to shoot him in Magadan. It's all the same to him how he dies. . . . Do you get me, Big Boy?' Svirko looks at me and laughs; looks me in the eye and asks me again, 'Get me?' So I tell him, 'Sure Comrade Chief, that's what I say—maybe it's better if he gets it over with right away. Why make him suffer?'

" 'Right! You've got the idea,' answers Svirko, and he claps me on the shoulder. 'I can see that you're a boy with a head on your shoulders. I wasn't mistaken in you. I'll be taking you out of the guard one of these days, and appointing you chief of a camp sector. If you try to keep your nose clean, do what's right, you'll go right to the top! But see to it that you do your duty. If he tries to escape, shoot him, and do it so that everything is legal. I don't have to spell it out. You should know your business well enough.'

"I was on my way out when he stops me and asks, 'Who's going with you as the second guard?' I told him I didn't know who would be appointed. Svirko gave me more cigarettes and a bottle of vodka and said, 'Give this to your sergeant. Ask him to appoint the same soldier who was on guard duty at the prison. One outsider's enough for this job. But get it across to him not to talk about things that are none of his business. When Voskoboinikov runs away, and you shoot him, it would be better that the other one didn't see it. Fix things so that everything comes off right. You'll know how better when you're out there.'

"I understood what Svirko wanted. When I was alone I started to realize how terrible it was, what I had to do. I asked the sergeant to send the soldier along with me to Magadan. I said he was a friend of mine. I gave him the bottle of vodka and the cigarettes, and said that somebody had sent them to me from Magadan in a package. I promised to bring him something else back from Magadan.

"The whole night I couldn't sleep. I thought all the time about what I had to do. If I didn't do it, Svirko would ruin me. If I did do it, it would be terrible! And then, I had to figure out how to do it so that the other soldier wouldn't see it. I thought the whole night, but I couldn't find any answers. In the morning we took off with Voskoboinikov. The whole day long, riding along in the snow, looking at Voskoboinikov, bundled up in the sleigh, I kept wondering, how I could do it. I thought of everything. I even played with the idea of killing both of them, so as to get rid of any witnesses. I would have said that Voskoboinikov went for my friend, grabbed his rifle away from him and shot, and that I shot him. I was thinking of riding on to Magadan and telling everything I knew, what I had seen, what I was being forced to do. Yes, and I also thought of shooting myself. It seemed to me that I couldn't fulfill this order, even if Svirko would ruin me if I failed.

"Then, along toward evening, we rode up to a little house standing by the road. Nobody lived there, but there was a stove, and other things for people travelling by to use. We stopped, left Voskoboinikov in the sleigh, and went into the house. Then it came to me all of a sudden. Now was the time to do it! I told the other soldier to start a fire and said I would go and fetch Voskoboinikov.

"I got out of the house. My hands, my feet are trembling, my heart's pounding. 'Now,' I say to myself, 'I'll set the horses galloping down the road, and then I'll shoot him as if he's trying to get away with the horses.' I opened the fur in which Voskoboinikov's all wrapped up. He's lying there, not moving. I poke him with my hand, to rouse him. Then I see he's dead. Suddenly I feel good all over. I feel happy. 'Thank God I won't have to do it after all,' I think.

"My first thought was to go back and report that Voskoboinikov died along the road. But then I realized that I couldn't do that. What did he die from? From his beatings! This would make things look bad for Svirko and I would be making plenty of trouble for myself.

"I rode away from the house with the body for a few meters, threw it out of the sleigh onto the road, and I beat the horses with the whip. They started galloping down the road. 'There's not a second to be lost,' I thought to myself, 'otherwise everything will fall through.' I pointed the rifle at the back of the dead man, but my fingers wouldn't do it. I couldn't shoot. The horses were galloping off, getting farther away, and there I was standing before Voskoboinikov and couldn't shoot. But I had to put a bullet hole in him. I pulled myself together and squeezed the trigger. I ran back a few steps, turned around and started running toward Voskoboinikov again, as if chasing him, and I started shouting and firing into the air. The other soldier jumped out of the house with his rifle in his hand, and not understanding what it was all about, also began to shoot.

"I went up to Voskoboinikov, trembling as if I had the fever. The other soldier came over and stood looking at me. 'What's the matter with you?' he asked me. 'I killed a dead man!' I told him, and it scared me, the way I said it."

Smirnov paused a moment, and then continued, "Every night I see that dead face! I can't sleep. I'm tired." He let his head fall on the table and began to sob. "Do what you want to with me, Comrade Commander! I can't stand it any more. Why did I shoot a dead man? What can I do now?"

Presently he began again: "We got back to Urutukan late in the evening. I went to Svirko. He was already in bed. He came out, and the first thing he said to me was, 'Well, how did it go?' But I couldn't answer him. He started to shake me by the shoulders, to bring me around, and kept saying, 'Talk, talk, damn it! Why don't you talk?'

" 'Vodka!' I said. He poured me a glass. I tossed it down and said, 'More!' He poured me more. I drank again. 'More!' I said. He wouldn't give me any more.

" 'Talk!' he said. 'How did it go?'

"I began to shout at him as hard as I could, 'I'll tell you! Give me more vodka!' Svirko poured me out a third glass, and put it in front of me. He stepped off to one side, and stood there looking at me, not saying anything. I glanced at him. His look scared me. 'Now he'll kill me,' I thought, 'I shouldn't drink the third glass.' My head was whirling, there was a buzzing in my head. I stood up at attention, saluted and said, 'Excuse me, comrade chief, I was worn out from the road. Everything's all right. Your order has been fulfilled one hundred per cent!'

" 'What do you mean, my order?' asked Svirko in a quiet voice.

" 'I shot Voskoboinikov!'

"Svirko frowned at me and said in a strange tone, 'I didn't order you to shoot Voskoboinikov.'

"I couldn't believe my ears. 'What do you mean, Comrade Chief? Why, you said yourself. . . .'

" 'What did I say? I said to you that if Voskoboinikov should run away, and if you couldn't catch him, that you should use your weapon, in accordance with regulations. I even asked you whether you understood your duty.'

"Suddenly I got boiling mad at Svirko. I felt like running him through with my bayonet. I guess he understood what I was thinking. He could probably see from the look in my eyes. When I looked at him he was standing there with a smile, holding a pistol in his hand, toying with it. I got hold of myself.

" 'So what happened?' asked Svirko.

"I answered him, 'During a rest stop Voskoboinikov tried to escape with the horses. The other guard and I opened fire on him and he was killed.'

" 'A pity!' said Svirko. 'He was supposed to appear before a court. But it can't be helped. You acted correctly, of course, according to the regulations. Report this to your commander. Turn the corpse over to the quartermaster, let them bury it. As for you, go to the *kaserne* and get some sleep. You're completely drunk! Come back here to me in the morning. Go now, and don't flap your tongue. Wait a minute.' Svirko tossed the pistol into the air, caught it again, clucking his tongue. 'What about the other soldier? Does he know anything?'

" 'No, he doesn't know anything. I mean, he knows that Voskoboinikov ran away. . . .'

"When I left Svirko I was weak in the knees, hardly able to walk. I don't remember how I made it to the sleigh, out on the edge of the village. I don't remember carrying the corpse away. I don't remember coming back to the *kaserne*. I was drunk. I lay down and fell asleep. Late the next evening I came to Svirko again. I drank vodka with him. I told him everything, how it was. He was in a gay mood. He laughed a lot, and praised me. He gave me a thousand rubles, and said that he would take me out of the guard and make me a sector chief; not now, but later, after this business blew over.

"The commander put me under arrest for three days for reporting in drunk at the *kaserne*. Then they interrogated me in the operative-Chekist department. Svirko stood behind me, made them call off the investigation. My commander also interrogated me. He didn't believe what I told him. You see, he knows what Svirko did to Voskoboinikov during the interrogation. Then they arrested me and brought me here to you under guard.

"I don't know what will happen now, but it seems to look very bad for me. That's the whole truth. I didn't kill Voskoboinikov. I shot a dead man! He was looking at me with that bloody eye of his, where Svirko had stabbed him. I saw the stick stab his eye. I saw it in the keyhole. A dead man ran away! I shot a dead man! Funny, isn't it?" Smirnov began to laugh. The laugh turned into a hysterical cackling. The commander of the guard ordered him removed to the guardhouse and put into a solitary cell.

The telephone rang. A low bass voice was heard, "Berzin speaking. Where is the soldier Smirnov from Urutukan?"

"In the guardhouse, sir."

"Do not interrogate him. Turn him over immediately to the central isolation prison of the operative-Chekist department. I have already made the necessary arrangements there."

"Yes sir!"

"You will report immediately to me."

"Yes sir!"

* * *

On the following day Svirko rode back to Urutukan. The commander of the guard unit from Urutukan, after having finally arrived in Magadan, did not return to his unit. He was transferred to a unit in the deep *taiga*, in the most remote camp sector, where there was no road as yet.

In the operative-Chekist department in Magadan a new dossier was opened. On its cover was written in bold letters:

FORMER SOLDIER OF THE GUARD
Ivan Nikolaevich SMIRNOV

The dossier began with a secret report of Chief of the Urutukan Camp Sector Svirko, addressed to Berzin. Svirko had written:

> . . . Before sending the accused prisoner Voskoboinikov to Magadan for trial, inasmuch as I felt this criminal to be especially important, *I personally* instructed senior soldier of the guard Smirnov. I reminded him of the necessity of

guarding Voskoboinikov *vigilantly*. I warned him to observe strictly the standing regulations for escort guard duty.

On the day following his departure soldier Smirnov, in a state of complete intoxication, returned to Urutukan with Voskoboinikov, whom he had killed along the way. He declared that Voskoboinikov had attempted to escape, and that during this attempt he was shot. For appearing in the *kaserne* in a drunken condition Smirnov was arrested by his commander and placed in disciplinary confinement for three days. I subsequently established the fact that soldier Smirnov deliberately shot Voskoboinikov in order to avoid making the lengthy journey to Magadan.

I consider soldier Smirnov to be particularly culpable in having deliberately murdered an important criminal awaiting trial. By his act Smirnov destroyed information which could have led to the uncovering of an anti-Soviet conspiracy whose existence was known, and to the identification of its participants.

On Svirko's report was written in Berzin's hand, "Expedite processing. Bring bandit Smirnov to trial. Punish severely."

The next document in the dossier was the report of medical examination of Voskoboinikov. After a detailed anatomical description of the corpse was the statement, "Death occurred as a result of bullet wound inflicted at close range. Aside from the wound and powder burns there was no evidence of violence found on the corpse."

After the medical report were the protocols of the interrogations and all kinds of notes corroborating Smirnov's guilt. His own statements concerning Voskoboinikov's death were directly refuted by the medical report. His statements concerning Svirko were also refuted. There were no witnesses to support them. His denials of guilt were regarded as the usual ruse of the criminal to escape punishment.

By Berzin's order the inquiry was brought to a close in the very shortest time. The formalities of administrative processing were accomplished with the minimum of delay.

The other soldier did not figure in the case. His statements were quite insignificant. He had not seen Smirnov shoot Voskoboinikov, and he remembered very well the words of the old experienced soldier, "Don't flap your tongue." He strictly observed this wise advice. After the very first interrogation they freed him and appointed him to serve in a remote unit of the guard force. All the others who had knowledge of the matter also kept prudently silent.

They did not even bring Smirnov before the court during the handling of his case at the special session. The sentence was decreed, as is usual in cases of this type, in the absence of the accused. Smirnov remained in the solitary confinement cell for the condemned in the central isolation prison in Magadan. It was forbidden for anyone to talk with him, even the guard.

In his cell he conducted himself quietly and with complete indifference. He moved about very little, remained quiet, spent most of his time sitting on his cot, staring vacantly. He never closed his eyes, day or night. The guards would often hear him whispering to himself, over and over, "I killed a dead man . . . I killed a dead man. . . ."

When they came for him one night, to take him out and shoot him, he suddenly came to himself and regained his senses. He understood immediately what was about to happen. He offered stubborn resistance, and would let nobody come near him. When they tried to seize him, he struck out with incredible strength, swinging his giant fists and legs at anyone who came within reach, screaming and cursing.

They finally overpowered him, tied him up and covered his eyes with a cloth, and carried him out.

* * *

In the spring, with the opening of navigation, Berzin went for a vacation on the Black Sea Coast, to rest and recuperate his strength. Svirko went with him, and did not come back to "Kolyma." Through Berzin's influence he was able to obtain appointment to a high post in Moscow.

MEDVED'

I

On "Kolyma," as they call the huge camp which is officially designated "Sevvostlag,"[1] and which occupies a vast territory in far-off Yakutia, in the northeast corner of the Soviet Union, in the wild, god-forsaken, untamed *taiga*, a rumor spread about which gave rise to many speculations. In the camp was expected the arrival of the former chief of the Leningrad administration of the NKVD, Medved', together with a group of his closest assistants—important Chekists,[2] who had been sentenced for having permitted the assassination of S. M. Kirov, Secretary of the Leningrad Party Committee, in December 1934.

At first people spoke cautiously about this, quietly, and only in the circles of the highest ranks of the camp administration, but soon the rumor spread about, and every one knew about it, even the most distant outposts of the camp out in the taiga. The name Medved' was quite well-known in the Soviet Union, and not only in NKVD circles. Here was a tried and true old Chekist, a companion-in-arms of Dzer-

[1] "Sevvostlag"—Northeast Corrective Labor Camp of the NKVD.

[2] Chekist—Appellation used in the USSR for operative workers of the organs of state security.

zhinsky[3] and Menzhinsky,[4] a favorite and henchman of Stalin himself. The sentencing and exile of Medved' together with his circle of intimate Chekist comrades to "Sevvostlag," considered to be one of the largest and most remote camps of the Soviet Union, with exceptionally difficult conditions of existence for the prisoners, was a great event, an extraordinarily important matter for all inhabitants of the camp.

Many guesses and conjectures were expressed as to what effect would be made by the presence of this "honored prisoner," a former highly-placed personage, who in his time had been on a height completely unattainable for the masses. How to handle this group, and on what work to employ them, were questions which disturbed many persons of the camp administration. It seemed inconceivable to thrust shovels and wheelbarrows into their hands and put them to general labor; it seemed improper to house them in the general barracks with the other prisoners, under armed guards. Every chief in the camp hoped privately that fate would spare him from the task of having under his care "prisoners" such as these. These questions disturbed not only the lowest and middle administration of the camp, but also the highest ranking officials—even Berzin himself, the chief of Dal'stroy,[5] (as the outpost of "Kolyma" was officially designated, in order to limit public knowledge of the existence of hundreds of thousands of prisoners by means of whose forces was accomplished the development of this uninhabited wild *taiga*, and with whose strength the great

Founder of the Soviet organs of state security in 1917.
Dzerzhinsky's successor to the post of Chief of the

breviated designation for *Dal'novostochnoe Stroitel'stvo*
struction [Administration].

construction projects were engineered). But except for a short official notification of the impending arrival of Medved' and the others, there was no guidance from Moscow; instructions concerning the matter were awaited from day to day.

Medved' was scheduled to arrive at "Kolyma" in the spring, with the opening of navigation, on the first steamship from Vladivostok into the Bay of Nagaev, on the coast of the Sea of Okhotsk. Usually navigation closes every year in December. The Bay of Nagaev freezes over, and until May no communication exists except by radio. In May navigation is opened again, and the ice-breaker "Krasin," of the Pacific maritime fleet, cutting through the ice, leads in the first caravan of ocean-going ships bringing new tens of thousands of prisoners, supplies, volunteer employees assigned to "Kolyma" and persons returning from leave. Everybody was impatiently awaiting news of the arrival of the first caravan.

Finally the long-awaited day arrived, and radio station Dal'stroy received notification of the approach of the ships. As was always the case, the majority of the population was at the port. This day was a great event—a kind of holiday for the residents of Magadan, the small town located two kilometers from the Bay of Nagaev, where the central administration of Dal'stroy, Sevvostlag, and other departments were located. Everybody went out to the port to meet arriving friends and acquaintances, to learn the news, to receive letters and packages which had been awaited the whole winter long. The first ship caravan was always met by a crowd of about a thousand officials of the camp and members of their families. The arrival of this particular caravan, however, was especially portentous because of the arrival of Medved', sentenced to imprisonment in the camp.

The ice-breaker "Krasin" approached slowly, its movement hardly noticeable, cutting through the thick icy cover of the bay. The ice crackled, crumpled, and great chunks fell roaring and crashing into the water or slid out onto the uncut surface. Following one another at intervals of a few hundred meters along the narrow corridor made by the icebreaker, went the great ocean-going steamships. From a distance it was easy to make out the great "Ualen," well-known to everybody, a freighter which had been adapted for the transport of prisoners. It accommodated ten thousand persons, not counting other freight. At the end of the caravan it was possible to make out the fast-sailing, comfortable passenger ship "Soviet," on which were travelling officials of the camp and–Medved'.

The ships did not come up to the moorings, which were not adequate for the simultaneous unloading of several vessels. They halted in the middle of the bay, and their unloading was accomplished directly onto the ice.

II

From the passenger ship "Soviet" descending by means of a ladder, debarked the arriving officials of the camp and their families. They were checked through the border control. Several persons, border guard officers and responsible employees of the camp administration, boarded the ship. They were met on board by a Chekist with rhomboids[6] on

[6] Rhomboid–Geometrical symbol worn on the collar tabs of the uniform, covered with red enamel, indicating general officer rank in the Red Army and the organs of the NKVD prior to the introduction of epaulettes.

the collar of his overcoat. The group started toward the first-class cabins. They stopped at the door of one of the cabins, and the Chekist who had arrived with the ship knocked on the door. From within the cabin was heard a soft, calm voice: "Yes! Come in. . . ."

Three entered the cabin; the rest of the group remained to wait in the corridor. Inside the cabin on a divan sat a thickset, well-fed person with a beard, by his looks about fifty years old. He was dressed in a military uniform, but without insignia of rank. Across from him sat another, a tall, strongly-built one, with a clean-shaven, flabby face, dressed like the first. In two neighboring cabins were accommodated three more of the group who had arrived to serve out their sentence in the camp.

They had been accompanied from Moscow by only one Chekist, of general's rank, the one who had come out to meet the officials of the camp when they approached the ship. He was the husband of the sister of one of the Chekist prisoners whom he was escorting.

Not one of those who had been sitting in the cabin got up when the functionaries of the camp administration approached them, and only by a nod of the head did they answer the greeting of those who had entered. They behaved very importantly, spoke little, answered unhurriedly, with supercilious, unconcealed smiles. The functionaries of the camp presented themselves:

"I am Chief of the Accounting-Distribution Department of Sevvostlag," said one.

"Chief of the First Section of the Operative-Chekist Department," said another. A third was a representative of the border troops.

"I am Medved'. This is my colleague Zaporozhets,"[7] said the small person with the beard, indicating with his hand the one sitting across from him. "Where are you taking us now?" he asked.

"To Magadan, not far from the bay. There are five rooms reserved for you in the hotel, where you may make yourselves comfortable. The Chief of Dal'stroy and Special Plenipotentiary of the Collegium of the NKVD of the USSR Comrade Berzin has requested that you report to him tomorrow at ten o'clock in the morning. Automobiles will be sent for you; but today you will rest up from the trip . . . ," replied the representative of the camp administration in an obliging, ingratiating tone.

"Well, good. Let's go then!" said Medved', and with a grunt, nonchalantly he slowly got up from the divan, took from its hook a uniform coat with a fur lining, and began to put it on. Zaporozhets also started to collect his effects. Those who had come to pick up the new arrivals assisted them with alacrity. Zaporozhets waved one of them away, and smiling, said ironically, "Forget it. What's all the fuss—we're prisoners, aren't we?" The chief of the camp, with an embarrassed air, continued to assist his getting dressed with a polite smile on his face, which conveyed an expression of approval of the "joke" of the "prisoner."

"What about our baggage?" asked Medved', after he had dressed himself and they were all getting ready to leave the cabin.

The Chekist accompanying this special group of prisoners had already informed the other three officials about the collection of baggage, and there, standing in the corri-

[7] Zaporozhets—Name of the chief of the operative division of the Leningrad headquarters of the NKVD, sentenced along with Medved'.

dor, smoking expensive cigarettes, they all began to discuss how to handle the problem. Their baggage was not located in the baggage hold, but had been put in a neighboring cabin, and occupied so much space that it was impossible to enter. Here were assembled large travelling trunks, boxes and suitcases covered with canvas. These five prisoners had so much baggage that it was necessary to call for a truck to transport it. An armed sentry was finally stationed before the cabin to guard the effects, and they all moved toward the exit.

On the ice near the ship three automobiles were waiting. Medved' and his comrades and the accompanying officials of the camp got in, and the group drove off to Magadan, to the rooms reserved at the hotel. After a while a pickup truck drove up to the ship with ten unarmed guards from the camp. They loaded up the baggage and drove off with it.

Over the ice-covered bay there slowly stretched out from each ship toward the shore the long grey columns of several tens of thousands of prisoners. They were surrounded by convoy troops with slung rifles, and alongside them walked escort guards with dogs. In the air hung the special acrid prison-smell of carbolic, filth, sweat.

III

Several days passed. Medved' and his comrades continued to live in the hotel. They were often to be encountered on the streets of Magadan, strolling quietly, slowly in their military NKVD overcoats, on which were the marks of the symbols of rank and medals which they had formerly worn. They associated with no one and visited no one, and they in turn were seldom visited; except by the order of Berzin. The Chekist who had accompanied them had returned to Moscow, after turning them over to the custody of the Chief of Dal'stroy. When officials of the camp or personnel of the guard or soldiers of the border troops met them on the street, they respectfully greeted them in a military manner, rendering the salute. Prisoners upon meeting them took off their caps, bowing with servility.

They ate breakfast, lunch and dinner in the restaurant of the hotel, where they had their own table reserved exclusively for their use. They conducted themselves with an air of dignity and independence. Berzin, when riding out to the *taiga* sections of the camp, invariably took one or another of them along with him. Their authority had not been shaken.

Sometimes they would ride out of Magadan into the *taiga*, in order to do some hunting. They had brought with them a whole collection of hunting rifles and a great reserve of accessories, which were locally in very short supply and seldom seen on "Kolyma." Inveterate hunters from the staff of the camp who had been forced to limit their passion for the sport because there was no free sale of gunpowder, shot and other necessaries for the hunt, discovered that the former elite possessed a copious reserve of all that was necessary, and the officials not infrequently came to them with requests. They never received a refusal, until Berzin heard about what was going on, and categorically forbade it.

After a certain period of time had passed, Medved' and the others ceased to appear on the streets of Magadan. Only one former chief of the Special Section of the Leningrad Administration of the NKVD, Fomin by name, could still be seen every day along the road between the private house reserved for him and the building of the Operative-Chekist Section of Dal'stroy. He had been assigned to this department and actually directed all its work, which was responsible for the territory of the entire Kolyma region. The official chief of the Operative-Chekist Section continued to occupy his position only formally, and in fact became merely Fomin's assistant; subsequently he was obliged to yield his place to him entirely. Zaporozhets was appointed deputy of one of the administrations of Dal'stroy, and in fact he directed it. Two of the others also received important positions at branches of the camp in the *taiga*. Medved' was appointed deputy, and soon thereafter chief, of the road administration of Dal'stroy, which was conducting the construction of a first-class highway, over two thousand kilometers long, to connect the Bay of Nagev with the city of Yakutsk and the mouth of the Kolyma river.

The conditions which were established for all of them in their imprisonment on "Kolyma" differed really from those of the high officials of the camp administration and of Dal'stroy only to the extent that sufficiency is differentiated from luxury. Their importance and influence among the higher administration of the camp was so great that the authority of the highest camp officials could not be compared with it, except that of Berzin himself. The officials reasoned as follows: "These are very great people, whom Stalin knows personally. They are known in the Politburo of the Central Committee of the Party, and in the government. As a result of certain circumstances known only to the Party and to the government, it has been necessary to exile them for a certain length of time, for purely formal reasons, possibly for reasons of a very intimate character, known only to Stalin himself."

Everyone was astonished at the mild sentence which had

been meted out to these persons, for having permitted the assassination of Leningrad Party leader Kirov. Three years imprisonment is by Soviet standards an insignificant sentence. What was even more incomprehensible was the fact that such a light sentence had been meted out to such important figures as Medved', Zaporozhets, Fomin and the others who, after all, had been expelled from the highest posts of the NKVD. The Soviet people are accustomed to sentences of ten years imprisonment, and executions by firing squad for the smallest negligence. They are used to seeing persons sentenced to long years at the camps for unfriendly utterances about Party and government measures, for uncomplimentary opinions concerning the leaders, for telling anti-Soviet anecdotes. There was something incomprehensible about the present case, especially since everyone could plainly see the conditions under which these prisoners were living here in the camp. No one had any doubt that after three years they would all be reinstated in their former posts and would again enjoy the very same power, the same greatness, which they had possessed before their arrival at "Kolyma."

All this was only conjecture for the greater part, but as a matter of fact, it corresponded to a great extent with the facts, except for the part about what was in store for Medved' and his colleagues at the end of the three years. . . . But at that time, of course, no one could foresee this. Directly from this kind of thinking stemmed the attitude of everyone, including Berzin, toward them. Berzin himself from the very first day set the pattern for this attitude, and subsequently supported it. So it was clear then to all, that these were persons not only with a great past, but with an equally great future.

IV

I was riding along the highway under construction, on a truck which was going my way deep into the Kolyma *taiga*, on a survey of troop units. Along almost the entire length of the road, prisoners were working. Autumn was beginning, and the weather was getting cold. Already at night there were heavy frosts. Automobiles were moving slowly along the unfinished road, limiting their speed to thirty kilometers, and in places reducing it to ten or fifteen kilometers an hour. I was riding toward Urutukanu, and had already travelled about three hundred and fifty kilometers from Magadan during the fifteen hours of my journey, with short stops for eating and servicing the vehicle.

In Urutukanu was located the center of one of the *taiga* branches of the camp, and when I arrived there it was already night. The transport was not going further, and I decided to stop here until the next day. I got out of the vehicle and started toward the quarters of the chief of the camp administration department, whom I knew personally, hoping to stay with him for the night. Despite the fact that it was already ten o'clock, I saw that the windows of his office were brightly illuminated, and I proceeded in that direction. In the office, besides the chief of the department I found the head of the department for road construction, Medved'. I immediately recognized him, since I had seen him on the day of the arrival of his group at "Kolyma," and had encountered him several times in Magadan, although as yet I had never had occasion to speak with him.

We exchanged a few words, and upon learning that I had no place to sleep, Medved' considerately proposed that I stay with him for the night. As chief of road construction for the entire extent of the road he had his own small cottages, well-furnished, wherever he stopped on his trips along the construction project. Pleading fatigue, I started to set off alone for his cottage, but he also got up and began to take his leave of the department chief. We walked along together. On the way he questioned me as to who I was, and how I had landed on "Kolyma." I told him briefly about myself.

"You're a military man then? Well, that's fine, we'll talk about military things. I haven't had a chance to talk about this as yet since I've come to 'Kolyma,' " said Medved', apparently having decided to devote this evening to a conversation with me. We arrived at his place. In the small wooden cottage were three tiny rooms, decently furnished. In two of them stood beds; the third room served as a combined office and dining room. He invited me to have supper with him, and I did not decline. Using a military-type field telephone which was located in the room, he ordered a supper to be prepared and brought, and while we were waiting he took from a cabinet a bottle of pure spirits, which in the *taiga* is drunk in lieu of vodka and other strong alcoholic beverages, and which in winter is a necessity on trips through this wilderness. He reached for conserves and bread and, having laid out this modest "buffet" directly on a sheet of paper, we began to have a snack, continuing our conversation.

The *taiga*, the remoteness, the loneliness, the tedium, and finally, a secluded nocturnal conversation in a comfortable warm room with a drink, has the effect of disposing people well toward one another, and draws them out toward frankness. But you're not always alone in the *taiga*; the feeling for one another doesn't last forever; and furthermore, I realized what a tremendous difference existed between Medved' and myself. True, I was in uniform, and he had been deprived of the right to wear it; but this was the only right of which he had been deprived, and even this was only temporary, a fact which I also understood very well. All this forced me to be very cautious in my conversations, and to weigh my every word. He spoke little; instead he posed questions, and listened to what I told him.

A young girl prisoner, who worked in the camp kitchen for the officials, brought us our supper. She produced eating utensils and set the table. It was evident that she constantly served this little cottage and those who occupied it. Upon the girl's appearance Medved' abruptly changed the subject of the conversation and, after ordering breakfast from her for the morning, sent her away.

Our conversation stretched out far after midnight. The electric current, as is usual in the remote sections of the camp, was shut off at twelve o'clock at night. We continued our conversation by light of a kerosene lamp.

The good supper, the several drinks of spirits, the rare and interesting conversational partner in the person of Medved', made me forget about fatigue and sleep. I gladly conversed with him; I answered all his questions and told him everything which interested him. After two hours of our conversation I felt as if I already had been acquainted with him for a long time. He listened to me with great attention and interest. Gradually he became more talkative, and, becoming carried away by his recollections, he began to tell about himself, rather frankly, as it seemed to me.

In his tone, his words, his manner of speaking could be felt self-assurance, and now and then there crept in a certain bragging air. He made a point of emphasizing the importance which still remained to him, despite his formal status of prisoner. His injured ego and pride was clearly perceivable in many of his utterances. He offered sharp, audacious opinions concerning those in whose power he found himself on "Kolyma," and scrutinized critically everything which he saw here. He expressed himself with surprising frankness, sometimes almost with cynicism, concerning everything that was going on in the camps. His observations and assessments represented only his personal point of view, but this naturally coincided completely with that of the powers who mold the destinies of the nation, and with whose number he had so recently had a close relationship. Stalin himself was among them, of course, and with him Medved' had also frequently had occasion to converse about many things. The genuineness of these views and opinions must have been unassailable.

This strange situation in which I found myself was one wherein two persons from one society, but belonging to very different planes thereof, separated by great differences in rank, turned out for the moment to be equals as the result of a series of circumstances which had brought about this sequestered, candid conversation. Outwardly I behaved very correctly, and accorded Medved' the respect due him. Nonetheless, during the course of our conversation that night, the difference in our stations was gradually erased, and presently I began, quite without embarrassment, to pose questions to him on matters of which I was not certain, in order to hear what answers he would give. And he, for his part, answered me simply and frankly. He talked about things which it was not proper to discuss aloud, things concerning which at that time I could not have had even the slightest conception. I was astonished by what I heard from the lips of this man.

V

"So then, my young friend," he said good-naturedly, with a nuance of condescension, "you say that you landed on 'Kolyma' quite recently, and that, for you, as a fresh arrival here, a new world opened itself up. The understanding of it all depends on one's outlook, and not upon one's knowledge of the details. Formerly, before my arrival here, I did not know how the utilization of prison labor was accomplished in all its particulars within the socialist structure of our state. But although the details were not clear to me, I knew generally what was going on, and recognized its necessity even despite the fact that it was all being done at the price of many millions of human beings, who were being deliberately, intentionally consigned to death.

"Comrade Stalin says: 'The death of one person—this is a tragedy. The perishing of millions—is statistics.' This is true!

"In order to transform society in the state, in order to remake the world and achieve the victory of communism, great sacrifices and many victims are unavoidable; we consciously, deliberately accept this. In politics nothing is achieved easily, and the transformation of human society throughout the entire world will demand colossal sacrifices. The shorter the period in which these are accomplished, the sooner will the goal be reached.

"A few decades from now the new generation will be completely ignorant of these sacrifices, which will have been responsible for their new way of life. The new generation will study the history of the building of communism without concerning itself with these statistics. They will not need to have knowledge of them. They will be the possessors of all the blessings of life, and they will be the masters of the world. They will eulogize us, the builders of communism today, us, their forefathers, who created a happy life for them. They will not inquire as to the price at which all this was achieved. They will be people with new understandings and viewpoints, with new ambitions; they will be the citizens of the world communist society.

"We are making use of these 'statistics' to whatever extent is necessary; we are exploiting human resources in our plans for the realization of new possibilities—we are conceiving, creating! We are building communism, and will continue to build it to the end, regardless of all difficulties and sacrifices. At any cost, by any means we shall proceed to the predetermined goal, by the shortest course!

"You are aware that as early as 1922 Comrade Stalin said, 'The Union of Soviet Socialist Republics—is the prototype of the World Soviet Socialist Republics.'[8] This is quite true! We have been striving toward this goal for eighteen years already, and we shall never stop! We shall achieve it at any price! But great willpower is needed for this, and Comrade Stalin and we Bolsheviks possess it. Strong nerves are needed, and decisiveness, tenacity, audacity of intention and decision—if you like, even ruthlessness. The weak, the timid, the indecisive are destined to failure and death; the strong, the daring—to victory! To achieve our goal we re-

[8] This declaration was made by Stalin in December 1922 at the first congress of the Union of Soviet Socialist Republics, and is found in his Collected Works, Volume 5, page 158.

ject all moral standards. This is our principle. Morally we endorse everything which serves the dictates of the situation, in our battle for existence, for the realization of our goal. The end justifies the means. That's the way we think, we Bolsheviks!

"Our goal is the triumph of communism throughout the world. We are creating a great thing; can we afford to hesitate because of the number of sacrifices which must be made? . . . Let the cost run, if necessary, even to millions of our contemporaries. We are now laying down the foundation for a bright future. We shall erect world communism on this foundation, even at the price of additional millions of lives, if need be.

"Take 'Kolyma,' for example. At most three, four years ago there was a wilderness here, uninhabited. Today a grandiose construction is under way at full speed. Cities are being built, and electric stations, railroads, highways, factories, workshops. Gold is being mined. . . . A year ago only a hundred thousand prisoners were working here, and today there are already five hundred thousand of them, and still the worker force is inadequate. In two, three years, there will be three million prisoners here, and if necessary, even five, ten. . . .

"Berzin is complaining about the great mortality and the inability of the prisoners to perform at maximum efficiency under the severe climatic conditions here. But it is not the perishing of people which bothers him. No, that's not it. What bothers him is that this reduces his labor force, which he needs so badly. In the course of a year ten per cent of the camp population dies. This amounts to fifty thousand persons today, but when the time comes that there are three million here, the mortality will be three hundred th-

prisoners per year. This loss of labor force is of course a great pity. We shall never be able to restore the fitness of the laborers, nor even to establish conditions which will curtail mortality. In America worn-out automobiles are not overhauled; they are simply replaced by new ones. It is more practical; automobiles are in abundance there. Likewise, it is to our advantage to obtain new, fresh labor forces in place of those which have been undermined. Our human resources are uncounted, but they represent an asset for us only in their role of labor force; and even this only so long as they may be utilized fully on the construction projects.

" 'Kolyma' gives the state gold; this is essential for us. Do you know how much gold is mined here? The chief of the planning section of Dal'stroy told me that in 1933 the plan for mining gold on 'Kolyma' was set at eight tons a year, and was fulfilled with ease. For 1934 it was doubled, and the sixteen tons specified were also mined without special efforts. In 1935 the plan for mining was raised to thirty-two tons a year and this also is easily being fulfilled today. In future years the plans will be increased ever more and more. They are being made already, based on approximate calculations as to the possibilities for their fulfillment. The treasures of the bowels of 'Kolyma' have not yet been exploited, and therefore at present in whole districts of gold fields on Srednikan[9] and in other districts of 'Kolyma' it has been necessary to curtail operations. Moscow has forbidden the conduct of mining operations on them, since during the past two years the yearly norms have been fulfilled without the necessity of deep working of the veins here on 'Kolyma.' The thing was accomplished merely by strip

[9] Srednikan—A gold region on "Kolyma," two hundred and fifty kilometers from Magadan.

mining, for the greater part, that is, by mining only the gold which was located on the surface of the earth or at a shallow depth. Meanwhile, in the deeper veins the gold deposits remained untouched. This barbaric, plundering exploitation of the gold-bearing regions was perpetrated only for its statistical effect. It was wanton sabotage. It has kept us from developing the gold resources, from locating the deposits and developing them. The yearly doubling of the plans for gold mining, and conservation of the new districts has compelled Berzin and the technicians here in the gold industry to go deeper into the veins, to work over more thoroughly the regions which have already been exploited. Berzin doesn't like this; it is plain to be seen. Nonetheless, he has been obliged to return to those areas which he had already once declared to be completely exploited and abandoned, though in fact countless riches still remained. Even under these conditions the significantly stepped-up norms have still been met, although at the cost of a certain amount of effort. Numerous geologic-prospecting parties, working now in the deep *taiga*, are finding ever newer gold deposits, and silver, lead and other valuable minerals; but all this will be exploited only in the future. Everything which the veins are capable of giving must be taken from them. Nothing must be left.

"This unexplored region of 'Kolyma' has brought to Berzin unearned praise. He has achieved it by picking up the gold which was scattered on the ground. And now this has become known to our government. Unrestricted power and authority were given to Berzin. 'Do whatever you want,' he was told, 'only mine gold, develop "Kolyma."' And now the time is coming to have a look at what might have been done here, and to compare it with what has actually been accomplished. Despite the fact that the results of the work accomplished by Berzin have exceeded all expectations, he has not done what he could have done, and what he should have done!

"Berzin is complaining about the inadequacy of the worker force to take from 'Kolyma' everything which could be taken, and to perform all the construction here which is needed to get the job done. Now he is asking for millions of prisoners, and in a year even this will not be enough for him. But people don't spring up so easily and quickly as gold on 'Kolyma.' Besides, there are still other reasons which make it difficult to procure the necessary number of people and the transport, materials, stores for the support of life, and construction which are necessary for the utilization of these people. In our nation everything is done to overcome these difficulties. Stalin says: 'Technology decides everything during the period of reconstruction. . . . Cadres, cadres and still more cadres. . . . Transport! That is our weak point.' These are significant words, and one must understand them, but not as the man in the street does. In these words is buried the deep meaning of that which you and I are witnessing, away out here on 'Kolyma', and of course, 'Kolyma' is only one small part of all that is being done in our land.

"If in our country priority of attention is given to the development of heavy industry and transport, then just as much attention should be, and positively will be paid to the production of new people–cadres, the future builders of communism. This is a very important and difficult problem, considering the limited living standard of our population, and this problem–that of increasing the population–

may be solved only by means of legislation, and put into practice only by the sternest of measures, such as the forbidding of abortions and severe punishment for their perpetration, taxes on those without children and families, encouragement of families with many children, and especially the mothers—all this is to be decreed in the very near future. The establishment of a broad system of children's homes, crèches, asylums and the like—these are not simply humanitarian measures, though the people may think that this is so, if they choose; this is an essential step for us in the attainment of the socialist structure. We need cadres, we need labor forces, and there are not enough of them. With every year, as the development of the building of our state proceeds, this shortage of worker hands is felt more and more acutely. If we do not take measures right now, we shall choke on our accomplishments, reverse our progress, and catastrophe will be the result.

"All this retards our tempo, and does not permit us the possibility of developing fully. Life does not wait; one must hasten, and stop for nothing, in order to achieve success. If one becomes squeamish about the great mortality rate and tries to avoid it, this slows the tempo, increases the expenditures and limits the possibilities.

"The prisoners in the camps are fulfilling the production norms. True, they are overtaxing their strength under pressure of the regime established here in the camps. They are perishing, and at the cost of their lives is being accomplished that which is necessary for us. But it is not just here; all over the country the toilers are overtaxing their strength on labor under the pressure of one form of coercion or another—socialist organization of labor, socialist competition, and the like. Only recently a new form of raising labor productivity has appeared—the Stakhanov movement. It will have a great future. For the time being the effectiveness of the population as a working force is being curtailed by these measures. This is to be expected; it is inevitable for the ultimate success of our program.

"The people of today are doomed to self-sacrifice; they are offered up for the sake of fulfillment of the great Stalinist plans. At the same time they are suffering limitations and shortages, and their living standard is on a low level. This also is unavoidable. The life of every person, his well-being, his home, must be completely dependent upon the state, otherwise he will not have the necessary interest for participation in the building of socialism. If there is no strict state regime there will not be full submission, and if there is no severe punitive policy there can exist no power, the power which is needed to drive ahead the building of communism within the shortest possible time, and which can completely subordinate to itself the entire population of the country for this purpose. The stronger we become, the more capitalist enemies we shall have, and therefore we must oppose our force to them in the form of our industry and military potential—our Red Army. . . .

"This last remark concerning the army I made especially for you, my friend, so that you, as a military man, would also perceive the essentiality of your participation in the building of communism. . . ."

Medved' made a pause and, smiling, looked me straight in the eyes, then asked, "Well, how about it, do you agree with me?"

It seemed to me that he was testing me, laughing at me.

VI

I listened to Medved' with great attention. Everything that he said seemed unbelievable to me. In my naïveté and inexperience I wondered, "Is he sane? Was it not for such views that he was removed from the post which he held, and exiled to this place under some suitable pretext? It cannot be that our Soviet government, the party, Comrade Stalin, all think as does this fallen Chekist." This was the first time in my life that I had been obliged to talk on such a theme with a person who had stood close to our supreme power, and I was thunderstruck. But my doubts were dispersed when I recollected everything which I had already seen on "Kolyma." It all confirmed what Medved' had said. That which I had considered to be distortion of the punitive policy in the camps of "Kolyma" turned out to be a profoundly thought out system, recognized as necessary in our Soviet state. For the second time in my life, doubts arose. (The first time had been in 1929-1930, during the period of collectivization.)

I was thunderstruck by the daring and cynical frankness of Medved' and his opinions. Why was he talking to me about all this? How could one dare to say such things, even if they were true? Evidently it was permissible to express such opinions within that circle of state functionaries to whose number Medved' had belonged such a very short time ago, and now, in speaking about it, he was simply following his usual custom. Naturally he would never have started to talk about this with me had it not been for the peculiar position and unique circumstances in which he found himself. That evening a stream of opinions burst from him, and he forgot himself, flushed as he was from the several glasses of spirits he had consumed. I thought, "It's not possible that everything he has said could be attributable solely to drunken maunderings. With such a person as he, the centers of reticence may be released under the influence of the alcohol which he has drunk, the tongue may be loosened, but what he has said undoubtedly corresponds to the actual state of affairs."

Medved' continued: "Berzin . . . a strong man. Determined, decisive, hard. A real Bolshevik. He is deterred by no moral qualms whatsoever in the accomplishment of the great task assigned to him. He is a superb organizer and manager, and enjoys great confidence and reputation with the party and with Comrade Stalin as a competent, devoted and excellent Bolshevik-Chekist. We have few such people, and we need them badly at present. Broad powers have been given to him, and here on 'Kolyma' he is absolute sovereign. Back in Moscow they even call him 'The Kolyma King.'

"Here on 'Kolyma' is a state within a state. Here Soviet rule does not exist. Instead, all legislative and executive power is located in the hands of Berzin and his administrative apparatus, which is limited only to an insignificant degree by orders and instructions of the People's Commissar,[10] which however are not always observed, and are skillfully circumvented whenever this is necessary in Berzin's interests. On 'Kolyma,' in Berzin's kingdom, there exists a population in the form of the prisoners and the volunteer employees with their families, a state apparatus—an administration, its own procuror's office, court, army, police, its

[10] In this case was meant the People's Commissar for Internal Affairs of the USSR of that time, Yagoda.

own laws, its own railroads, its own river and sea fleet, aviation, cities, villages, electric stations and so forth. All this is subordinated to one man—Berzin.

"A few years will pass and this region of 'Kolyma,' separated by a thousand kilometers from the nearest inhabited Soviet soil, located almost fourteen thousand kilometers distant from our capital, will be absolutely self-sufficient and independent, with its own developed industry and agriculture, and everything necessary for existence. It will have a population of several millions, and will actually be a kind of state of its own, exceeding in its territory and population Finland, Sweden and many other European states.

"This is what 'Kolyma' means, and this is what Berzin has been assigned to do. Unlimited power has been given to him here, and in exchange for the gold which he delivers in abundance, no strict accounting has been demanded of him as to how and what he does here. At present no one interferes in his affairs. . . . Now, I'll tell you, it's best for the time being not to know this, but the fact is, that the time will come when Berzin will be called to account for a great deal. He is abusing his powers and the great confidence which has been placed in him; he feels himself indispensable; he knows his importance and even overestimates it. He shall not go unpunished for all this. The weight and significance of a man, his usefulness and his merits—that's one thing. But aside from this there is still another very important consideration which Berzin is not taking into account, and that is . . . well, let's leave it at that. I've chattered with you so much. . . . But I count on your good sense and discretion, and hope that I shall not regret our frank conversation of tonight. I was overcome by an insuppressible urge to talk—it burst through after a long period of restraint. . . ."

Medved' was silent for a long time, smoking a hand-rolled cigarette. He poured himself a glass of spirits, gulped it down, and chased it with water. He sat musing.

I also was silent. To take part in such a conversation and express my opinions for or against, was very risky for me. I was already in danger as it was, because of the consequences which would arise as a result of what I had heard from Medved', were it to become known.

"Now take Berzin, for example . . . an important man, an essential person, and all that sort of thing," began Medved' once more, rousing himself, and addressing himself directly to me. "And what about me? Am I not an essential person? Am I superfluous? Not a significant personality? . . . I—Medved'! . . . What do you think?" All this he said in the tone of one who had been insulted, angered, injured. After a pause he continued again in a somewhat more tranquil voice, "I'll tell you; in December of last year, when Sergei Mironovich was assassinated, Comrade Stalin summoned me to Moscow and said, 'You were unable to protect the life of the leader of the Leningrad Party, our dear Sergei Mironovich Kirov. You committed an unforgivable negligence, which gave rise to the cause of his untimely death. You have been very culpable in this matter! For this I am depriving you of the powers which you have shown yourself unworthy to exercise. But your former services on behalf of the party, as well as your decorations, these I shall keep here with me, and after three years I shall return them to you together with additional ones. And now, go to 'Kolyma,' and put things in order there. Good-by, for three years!' " Medved's face bore an ironical smile, as he repeated these words of Stalin.

Suddenly, with a quick start, he jumped up, and struck

the table with his fist so strongly that the dishes and glasses jumped. He broke into a rage; his eyes suddenly became bloodshot, and his face turned purple. He shouted menacingly, "I know as well as Stalin how it was all pulled off! I know very well who killed Kirov, and I know how it was done!"

He fell silent then, and breathing heavily, set to walking about the room with long strides. I was shocked. I sat in silence on the divan, and did not lower my gaze from him. I thought to myself, "So this is Medved'!" I was frightened by these words of his, by his excited face, and by his terrible confession. . . .

"Enough! Let's get some sleep. Good night!" said Medved' to me in a voice which was already calm again. "I'll wake you up in the morning at seven o'clock and take you to Ust'–Utin' in my automobile. I'm also going there." He went into his room.

That is how my first and last conversation with Medved' ended, that night which was so important in my life, that night which laid the foundation for my realization of what was being perpetrated in our country, and what was so diligently being concealed from the people by the dictators in the Kremlin, these wielders of power, these unlimited and unaccountable masters of a state with a population of almost two hundred million, occupying one sixth of the world's area. How completely these facts contradicted the words of the mendacious Soviet propaganda about the concern of the state for the well-being of the toiling masses, about the peaceful creative work of the Soviet people, about the happy and joyous life of the laborers in the only socialist state in the world.

In the morning Medved' was again reserved and uncommunicative. It seemed to me that he was censuring himself for his excessive frankness with me the night before. Not with so much as a single word did he touch on the theme of the previous night.

After breakfast we got into his automobile and travelled further, deep into the *taiga*, along the road under construction. Prisoners were working on it. Medved' often stopped the automobile, got out, and conversed at length with the engineers who were directing the construction. Upon his appearance the foremen, the prisoners, and the volunteer workers bustled about, obligingly tried to anticipate all of Medved's wishes, respectfully answered his questions, looked searchingly into his eyes in anticipation of his decisions and orders. The guards and the commanders of the guard on duty stood to attention before him and, rendering the salute, stood ready to answer any question which he might direct to them. I knew that such deference as this was accorded no other person, with the exception of Berzin himself, on the occasion of his infrequent appearances. It was plain to be seen that Medved' made everyone understand quite plainly who he was. His position as a prisoner did not alter in the slightest his prestige and authority. Despite everything, he still remained a strong and influential person.

VII

Shortly after this, with the last ship before the closing of navigation, I left "Kolyma" for Moscow, and never saw Medved' again. In 1937 began the mass repressions over the entire country, which are known to the whole world. A year later the purge began to reach even the workers of the NKVD, these servants who had so faithfully fulfilled the assignments of the Party and Stalin, and had destroyed hundreds of thousands of people whom Stalin saw as enemies and ill-wishers. During this time, I found out later, Medved' was shot on "Kolyma" together with the colleagues with whom he had arrived in 1935. And later Berzin himself was shot, together with all those who were close to him. And many others, great and small. . . .

Beside the many enemies with whom Stalin ruthlessly settled accounts in those years, another source of danger to him were the "strong people," such as Medved', from his old Bolshevik guard, his specially trusted accomplices and executors of all the crimes which had been committed by him. They knew too much.

It would be well for those who today occupy the places of these fallen titans to remember all this. They are doing the very same things, and the same fate is in store for them. But not many of them are mindful of that which Medved' did not wish to finish telling me in our conversation, "The weight and significance of a man, his usefulness and his merits—that's one thing. But aside from this there is still another very important consideration, and this is. . . ." What Medved' did not finish saying, was the key to understanding the fate of many of Stalin's accomplices.

"The new generation must not know the means by which communism was built." The witnesses and participants in this evil business of Stalin, in a timely and systematic manner, have been destroyed.

WHAT WAS HER CRIME?

IN northern Kazakhstan the harsh winter was already beginning. Freezing weather was setting in, with sharp winds that pierced one through and through. A fine needle-like snow-flurry was sprinkling, drifting momentarily toward the ground, and then suddenly sent scurrying, whirling by the sharp gusts of wind, all over the *steppe*.

At a small whistle-stop some twenty-five kilometers from the city of Karaganda was located the reception point of the Karaganda concentration camp. On a great open square not far from the whistle-stop a group of armed soldiers of the camp guard was standing in formation by the side of the tracks. Nearby, walking up and down, shivering from the cold, exchanging abrupt, short phrases with each other, were some officials of the camp administration, who had arrived to receive an expected shipment of new prisoners. Everybody was becoming chilled from the long wait, and in order to keep warm they were trotting about and hopping up and down. They looked like children romping about with one another.

Presently a train of sixty to seventy converted freight

cars with bars at the windows and doors appeared around a bend. On every fifth car there was a platform on which two guards were standing with rifles in their hands. They were dressed in sheepskin coats with high collars, in valenok boots and great fur-lined gloves. Their faces were covered with leather masks, also fur-lined, which covered the entire face. They wore warm cloth caps with red stars on the forehead. Leaning against the handrail enclosing the platform, these sentries kept sharp observation on each of the cars under their care. The black leather protective masks, with eyes glittering under the glass of their goggles, gave them a sinister, inhuman, even terrifying appearance. The full-length sheepskin coats, worn on top of leather half-coats, made the soldiers seem enormous, formless, immovable. The rifles which they held in their hands looked like fragile little toys.

Searchlights had been installed on each side of the platforms on which the sentries were standing, and on the platform of the last car, in addition to the searchlights, a machinegun was mounted. On each of the platforms there was a field telephone which communicated with the other posts and with the passenger cars in the middle of the train, in which the guard was accommodated. From these outward signs and from the fact that the prison cars were under such diligent guard, it was evident that the prisoners being delivered belonged to the category known as "Especially Dangerous Criminals."

The train pulled up to the side track. Out of a passenger car stepped the chief of the convoy guard in a sheepskin shortcoat. On his head, despite the cold, was only a jauntily set cap with a red band around the crown, and a blue top.*

* Red cap band and light blue crown signifies the MVD troops.

The officials of the camp administration clustered around him, and the discussion of details concerning the delivery and reception of the prisoners began. From two passenger cars, dressed in fur short-coats and valenok boots, armed with rifles and revolvers, the soldiers of the convoy jumped out and lined up alongside the cars for which they were responsible. Several dogs also jumped out of the cars. On being freed from their leashes by their handlers they trotted about the assembly area, stretching themselves after the long period of almost complete inactivity in the train.

The transfer of the prisoners began. They were all led out of the cars and lined up four deep, in groups before the cars. A count-up began. Their names were called, and checked against their personal dossiers. The escort guards who had arrived with the prisoners surrounded them, ensuring that they did not break out of the formation, and that everyone stayed in his group. After the counting and personal check of the prisoners the old guard—from the train—turned them over to the new—from the camp.

This process of delivery and reception is long and tedious, and when the weather is windy and freezing, it amounts almost to torture. The prisoners stood there in their tattered rags and torn footwear, shivering, their faces blue from the cold, pressing close to each other, trying to warm themselves up a little. Those standing on the edges would take turns with those standing in the middle. Since they were not permitted to move about, the poor wretches would stamp their feet in place, and would try to warm their hands by blowing on them. At infrequent intervals in turn one group of prisoners or another would be led off to one side for one or two hundred paces, and then brought back again to their places.

Several of the prisoner groups consisted entirely of women. There were young ones among them, as well as old ones who had difficulty in standing. I was walking past the groups standing by the train, awaiting their turn. Suddenly a woman prisoner tore herself from one of the groups and, completely oblivious to the shouts and threats of the guards, ran up to me. She wanted to tell me something. One of the guards rushed up to drag her back to her place. . . .

* * *

"Please, please, I beg of you! Listen to what I have to say! Let me say a few words to you. . . ." She looked around fearfully at the guard who had come running up. "Don't let him touch me—— Just a few words, that's all," she implored, turning to me again.

The guard, seizing her from behind by the shoulder, threw her back with a sharp jerk. The rude push caused her to lose her balance and, not having the strength to right herself, she staggered a few steps, flailing her arms, and fell on the ground. With his face flushed and distorted with anger, the guard came up to the prostrate woman, unslung his rifle and quickly operated the bolt. "Get up!" he shouted in an enraged and threatening voice, pointing the rifle at her. The senior guard, with pistol in hand, came running up to assist the other. Their consciousness of the presence of the camp officials had the effect of making the guard more zealous in the fulfillment of their duty. They tried to make amends for this violation on the part of the prisoner in the presence of the officials. The chief means by which they could express this zeal was by mercilessness and brutality.

The woman remained lying on the ground, as if she had not heard the guard's words. She sobbed, and continued her entreaty. She stretched out her arms to me; to me—a person in military uniform—a complete stranger to her. She was in a condition of extreme agitation; it was evident that at that moment it made absolutely no difference to her what might happen. She wanted to tell me something, even though she didn't know who I was.

The guards standing on posts nearby stiffened; their faces suddenly became tense, evil-looking. As if by some kind of signal they took their rifles in hand and readied themselves to deal firmly with any further violations, or tricks on the part of the prisoners. But the prisoners stood submissively in their places, observing apathetically and with complete indifference the incident which was taking place.

"Let her alone. Return to your places," I told them. They withdrew. I went up to the woman. She got up from the ground slowly, and began to adjust her clothing. She was weeping, and murmuring something incoherent, as if to herself. Then she regained awareness of her surroundings, and began to excuse herself. She began to complain of the roughness of the guards.

"What did you want to tell me?" I asked.

She somehow pulled herself together, drew herself up, and began to tell me what she wanted. She spoke firmly and with outward calmness. Her persisting state of agitation was betrayed only by the nervous pressing together of her stiff cold hands which she was trying to warm up with her breath, and the tears which had thickened in her eyes. From her appearance one might have judged her to be twenty-eight or thirty years old, although at first glance she seemed considerably older. Her attentuated, exhausted pale face was dirty, the eyes were swollen. Nevertheless, her features were attractive. She was dressed in a shabby fur coat, torn in many places but evidently expensive at one time. It was gathered at the waist by a rope. On her legs were the black quilted wadded trousers, patched in several places, which the prisoners wore. She was wearing large canvas shoes with heavy wooden soles. Her head was wrapped in some kind of torn dirty rags which substituted for a shawl. On her back she was carrying a primitive knapsack made of patches, onto which was tied the inevitable tin can which served as convict table ware. She had not washed during the several days of the long journey from Moscow in the dirty locked prison freight car.

"Citizen Chief! I beg you to call me up for an interview. I must tell you something extremely important. My life depends on it. I can't talk about it now—not here. I have been sentenced by a special session to ten years for counter-revolutionary acts. My name is N. . . Call me please, as soon as you can. I beg you. When I tell you, you will understand how important it is. . . ."

I was at a loss. The fact was, that in my official capacity I simply did not have the right to interfere in matters concerning the prisoners. I explained to her that I did not have the right to accept any explanations whatsoever, and I advised her to refer her problem to the camp administration.

She looked at me with disappointment, and said in an imploring tone, "But certainly you would be able to pass on my problem to the proper place. You see, I don't know anybody here." She began to weep again. "I don't want to, I can't. . . . I don't have the right to speak with anyone about this. But I have to tell—I must. I don't have the strength to stand it any longer. I can't torture myself anymore. I'm at a dead end—I can't find a way out. I beg you,

Citizen Chief, call me. . . ." Her weeping went over into sobbing, and she became incapable of further speech.

I could see that what she wanted to communicate to me was vitally important to her. I couldn't help pitying this unfortunate woman. What secret could she possibly want to tell me? Half from pity, half to calm her, I promised that I would try to arrange to call her, even this very evening perhaps. Then, after writing down her name, I told her to go to her place.

When the transfer of the prisoners had been completed and everybody began to disperse, I went up to the chief of the transfer point, with whom I had been acquainted for a short time, and told him of my conversation with the prisoner. He was completely indifferent; the matter had little interest for him. On perceiving my interest however, he suggested to me that I call this prisoner today, right away. He said that I could talk with her in his office.

In the evening they led her into the office of the chief of the transfer point. She timidly entered, accompanied by a guard. She looked about the room mistrustfully. When she saw me sitting behind the desk however, her face cleared up. She tried to smile, twisting her lips into a kind of grimace. Her appearance had changed somewhat. She had succeeded in putting herself in order. She had washed herself, combed her hair, had rid herself of all the excess rags which had been indispensable to her during the journey, and had tried to make as decent an appearance as possible. From under the tattered fur coat it was to be seen that she was dressed in clothes which had once upon a time been good and expensive, but which were now worn out, rumpled and dirty.

"Thank you, Citizen Chief," she began, "I don't know how to express my appreciation to you for your assistance," and then she stopped and glanced uncertainly at the guard standing by the doors, and said softly, "If possible, I would like to speak with you alone."

"Of course," I answered, and sent the guard away. I invited her to be seated, took out a cigarette-case and placed it on the table in front of her.

She thanked me, and lit up a cigarette. She drew quickly and deeply on it, inhaling the tobacco smoke with intense enjoyment. She looked at me and smiled, passed her hand over her forehead and said softly, "I haven't had a cigarette for a very long time. I'm a bit dizzy at the moment, but it's nothing. I'll be all right in a minute."

I could see the confidence which she had in me and the great hopes she was laying on this interview. I said to her, "Before I listen to you, I want to warn you once again that it is most unlikely that I can help you. I'll tell you frankly, that I granted your request and called you here simply because I felt sorry for you. Actually, it was the actions of the guard, who so roughly handled you at the train, that facilitated it for me. It seems to me that in the passion of your despair you may for lack of caution commit a great mistake, one which could have serious consequences for you. I am prepared to listen to you, to give you advice, perhaps even to put in a word for you with somebody from the camp administration, but nothing more. Now, think about it for a minute. Wouldn't it be better for you not to disclose your secret until a more suitable meeting with someone from the camp administration?"

"No, no! Under no circumstances!" she exclaimed with fright, "I beg you, don't send me away. Give me a chance to tell you everything. . . . I don't know why it is, but I feel that you can understand me and help me, or at least give me good advice as to what I should do. I'm in a desperate situation—I have nobody to talk with. I beg you, spare me a little time to tell you— During the past months I have met such terrible people everywhere in these awful prisons; but you—I can see that you are an intellectual. You can understand me—" She stopped herself suddenly, as if she had said something improper. She began to excuse herself with a guilty smile. "I beg your pardon. Perhaps it annoys you to have me refer to you as an intellectual—but there's no harm done, is there?"

"Why certainly not. What's bad about that?" I answered.

"I haven't offended you? I'm glad that you understand me correctly. You see, some of your—that is, no, excuse me," she said in confusion, "I didn't mean it that way, not your people, but generally speaking, some people, are offended by this word, and often in anger, you know, use the term 'rotten intelligentsia' as a term of insult."

She was right. As a result of Soviet training many in the USSR had learned to experience a feeling of hostility and scorn for the intelligentsia. "Yes, that's so," I said. "Well, shall we get on to your business? I'm listening to you."

She finished her cigarette, and rested her head on her hands, reflecting a minute. Then she straightened herself up with an abrupt movement, and looked at me. "Please, may I ask how much time you can allow me?"

I told her that time was of no importance, and that I did not wish to limit her.

She thanked me, paused a few moments to collect her thoughts, and then began her story.

* * *

"My father was a professor, a scientist who worked in Moscow at a scientific-research institute. I lost my mother when I was quite young. I was married at twenty. My husband held a high position in the Party. Toward the end he was in charge of a department of the Central Committee. A daughter was born to us a year after our marriage, and two years later, a son. I devoted all my time and energy to our home, our family and the children. We had a large apartment. My father lived with us, and had his own room, in which he slept and received visitors, his colleagues and friends. In our part of the apartment an entirely different society used to gather—my husband's Party comrades.

"Although we all lived in complete harmony together, my husband and I lived a different life from that of my father. The circle of friends in which my father moved was entirely different from that in which my husband and I associated, and when, as happened occasionally, my husband's friends encountered my father's colleagues in our home, the atmosphere was always strained. Both groups felt themselves ill at ease and uncomfortable. Conversation would lag. As hostess I found these hours to be some of the most difficult of my life. Invariably on these occasions the conversation would turn to politics. On such matters my husband's comrades, being for the most part important party figures, would speak with fervor, often allowing themselves to be carried away, and arguing with one another. My father's friends, on the other hand, would listen with interest to the views expressed, and would passively support the conversation, but would never enter into the arguments. It often happened however, that an awkward silence would come over the group. We would feel relieved when the guests finally departed. The problem was tacitly understood very well by all of us, and so far as possible we avoided having these meetings. Ordinarily our guests and those of my father visited in different parts of our home.

"I loved my father very much. He had brought me up, reared me, and had taken the place of my mother. I also loved my husband. He was a partner and a dear comrade. I did not feel myself a stranger in either part of the apartment. Indeed, I was the only one who felt at ease both in the society of my father's friends and with my husband's party comrades. That's how the years passed with us.

"The trouble all began one day, when my father returned from the institute later than was usual for him. My husband had not yet returned; he always got home late in the evening. My father told me that a strange and very disturbing incident occurred at the institute–several professors, scientific workers, including even the director of the institute, had been arrested the night before. Among those arrested were people with important names in the scientific world, including some of our good friends who often visited with us. My father related further that after working hours there was a meeting held in the institute. It was announced that the arrested persons were 'enemies of the people,' 'saboteurs,' that they were participants in an anti-Soviet organization. At the meeting everyone was urged to exceptional vigilance, in order to expose any enemy activity directed at the undermining of our Party, our socialist worker state, the one and only in the world. A resolution was adopted at the meeting. In the resolution a lot was said about the indispensability of the workers rallying around the Communist Party and its Central Committee. The resolution castigated enemies of the people, saboteurs and all counterrevolutionaries. It concluded with a request to the government and the Central Committee of the Party to battle mercilessly with the enemies of the people and to punish them severely.

"My father said that the whole affair had produced a stunning effect on everyone. As for himself, I saw that he simply could not calm himself. He paced nervously about the room and, holding his head in his hands, kept repeating over and over to himself, 'My God! What's happened? It's all so incomprehensible. . . . How can they possibly be enemies of the people? What counterrevolution could there possibly be?' To me he said, 'I know all these people very well. Many of them I have known from the time they were students. For dozens of years I've worked side by side with them in the same laboratories. These are men of science, not politicians. Even their own personal life did not exist for them. Their every interest and thought was directed solely to scientific research. These are diligent toilers who have already lived out their lives. They have devoted them to science, and now they have come to their last years. To accuse these people of counterrevolution, of sabotage, is absurd; it's sheer madness. It would make just as much sense,' he said to me, 'as if somebody were to accuse you of crimes such as these, despite the fact that it's obvious that outside of your home and children you know nothing and have no wish to know. It would make as much sense to accuse your husband of counterrevolution and sabotage—your husband—an honored and important party worker—or me perhaps. Maybe I'm a counterrevolutionary too. Maybe I'm a saboteur and enemy of the people.' My father could not restrain himself.

"He went into his room and I heard him pacing up and down until late in the evening, talking to himself. After some time had passed I went to him, to quiet him, but he was silently sitting in an easy chair, lost in thought, hanging his grey head, and sighing heavily from time to time.

"My husband telephoned and told me not to expect him before morning. I wanted to tell him what had happened, but with my very first words he answered me that he knew all about it, and that we would talk about it when he got home. A feeling of fear crept over me. I felt a premonition of something terrible, something awful. I didn't go to bed, I sat up until morning waiting for my husband. There was a light in my father's room also.

"Early in the morning my husband came home. I told him about everything. My father came in, and the three of us sat up for a long time, discussing the matter. My husband told us that in our country a very large anti-Soviet counter-revolutionary organization had been uncovered. It was composed of enemies of the people, and even members of the government and the Central Committee of the Party were members of it. My husband said that it was not a surprise, that the Party had apparently known of the existence of this organization for a long time, and that the organs of state security had thoroughly investigated its activity, and had identified all participants. Now the arrests were beginning.

"My husband soothed us and tried to put on a happy air. He assured us that the party doesn't make mistakes. I saw, however, that he was privately worried, and was trying to conceal the fact.

"Several days passed. Every day fresh news arrived concerning the arrests of our acquaintances who worked with my husband and with my father. Each morning there would be somebody who did not report for work, and from that moment he would be referred to as a saboteur or an enemy of the people. Upon the arrest of these persons all the studies and the directions which they had prepared were nullified and withdrawn, even though they had been in effect the day before. In the institute the scientific works of the 'enemies of the people,' and the books which they had written, were withdrawn from the libraries. Everywhere people began to write denunciations of each other. Suddenly people remembered who had written and said so-and-so, who was associated with whom by common activity or personal acquaintanceship, and when. Friends and colleagues became afraid to associate together or even to talk to each other. People denied their relatives—children their parents, parents their children, once they were determined to have landed among the ranks of the 'enemies of the people.'

"The arrests, starting in Moscow among the high-ranking officials, rolled out over the country, and seized even the middle and lower levels of the population. Many important military and political workers, anticipating their arrest, or at the moment of their seizure, committed suicide. . . ."

I listened attentively to what this woman was saying to me. I was able to supplement her terrible story mentally by that which was personally known to me. It was difficult for me to differentiate between what she was telling me and what I was supplying from my own personal knowledge. It was all true, just as she was telling me, without any exaggeration whatsoever. She continued:

"Every day, when my husband would come home from work, we would sit up late into the night and talk about what was going on in the country. My father was completely depressed, and was unable to rouse himself from his despair. Mechanically, from the habit of many years, he continued to go to the institute every day, but he was in no condition to accomplish anything in his laboratories. My husband had changed a great deal also. He was morose, irritable and uncommunicative. All his former energy, enthusiasm and conviction had disappeared completely. He became pensive, and often communicated to us the doubts and uncertainties which were assailing him.

"It happened one night. I was sitting up late with my father, as usual during the recent events. The children were already asleep. Suddenly noise and strange voices were heard in the vestibule. Our servant burst into the room terrified and informed us that something had happened—my husband had arrived, and some kind of military people were with him. My father and I went to meet them. In the vestibule armed men with red and blue caps were standing at the door. Others, also in uniform, were unceremoniously walking about through the rooms. My husband, pale and silent, was sitting on the divan in his study. Several of the men were rummaging in his desk and in his bookshelves, turning the contents upside down, making a search.

"As soon as we appeared, they took my father immediately off into his room. I flew to my husband, but they wouldn't let me near him. Trying to comfort me, he said in a strange voice, 'Don't be alarmed, there's been a mistake. Everything will come out all right.'

"They led me into the bedroom and told me to stay there. At the door there stood an armed soldier, who wouldn't even permit me to go to the cupboard and take anything out of it. The children were awakened by the noise and the loud talking. They were brought to me in the bedroom. Toward morning they put me and the children in the dining room. Everything was in disorder there after the search, scattered about in disorder. Even the curtains at the windows and the pictures had been taken down and lay scattered about on the floor. They began to conduct a search in the bedroom. They brought our servant into the dining room where I was sitting with the children. Up to then she had been under separate guard. She told me that they had taken my husband and my father away several hours ago. Throughout the whole apartment they now started to make a meticulous search, tapping out the floor, the walls and the ceiling. They questioned the servant, and paid particular attention to the names and addresses of our acquaintances who were accustomed to visit us. The search continued all night. In the morning they packed into an automobile several parcels of papers which they had confiscated.

"I was ordered to take the most essential things and move with the children into the servant's room next to the kitchen. The servant quickly packed her things and departed for her home in the village. The apartment was sealed. The Chekists departed, after ordering me to appear that same day at eight o'clock in the evening at the 'Lubyanka.' They gave no answer whatsoever to all my questions concerning my husband and my father.

"In the evening I reported to the NKVD. They knew about me already in the Commandatura. I was issued a pass, and I reported to the office which had summoned me. I was interrogated. When I finally got home it was after midnight. I had been unable to find out a thing concerning my father and my husband. On the following day I went to the NKVD on my own initiative, in order to see what I could find out, but I was refused even a pass. At the special window where information concerning arrestees is given out, they would tell me nothing. For several days after that I continued to go there in the desperate hope of learning some bit of news. I met many other unfortunate women there, in the same situation as I was, seeking some bit of information about their arrested husbands, fathers or children. I met women from all kinds of families, from generals and the highest government officials down to ordinary clerks. They were all in the same position. The people at the NKVD referred to us all simply as 'family members.' It was only later that I learned what this ominous name meant: 'Family members of traitors to the homeland.' From these unfortunate people I heard terrible things. I was in complete despair, and for the first time in my conscious life I turned to God in prayer. Are they all really enemies of the people? How can this possibly be true?

"After several days our apartment was taken over by new occupants. Some high-ranking officer of the NKVD moved into it. I had to move to a small room on the edge of the city. Now poverty was added to my other sufferings."

During the course of her story the prisoner was several times forced to stop, overcome by the emotions aroused in her by her memories. She would calm herself, and continue to speak again. She spoke quickly, in bursts. Sometimes she would stop and excuse herself for the acid remarks which spontaneously came from her lips concerning those who had brought her so much sadness and suffering. With sincerity and conviction she exclaimed, "If only Comrade Stalin knew about all this! He wouldn't permit such injustice. . . ."

The chief of the transfer point came into the office and informed me that the prisoners who had arrived that day would now be fed, and given a bath and a medical inspection. He requested that I release the prisoner, promising to give me the opportunity to continue the conversation the next day. It was midnight already, and I parted with the prisoner, after having agreed to see her again the next day.

"What's she telling you?" the chief of the transfer point asked with mild interest. I was not in a mood to talk about it and I gave him a non-committal reply. I had become interested in the history of this prisoner, and I decided that I would not go home tonight, but remain here until the following day.

I couldn't go to sleep. I dreamed about what I had just heard. I remembered a lot of things that were known to me from personal experience in those awful years of repression. I thought about myself, about some of my brother officers of the Red army, and about my friends and acquaintances. I thought about all those poor wretches who had been touched by that dread fever, the terror of Stalin.

My mind turned to the fate of my old wartime commander Nikolai Nikolaevich Krivoruchko, who had already distinguished himself as early as the Civil War. He was an old communist, honored by the revolution and by the Soviet government, a cavalry corps commander. He had been arrested quite recently as an enemy of the people. During his interrogation the NKVD investigator began to beat him, demanding that he sign a false confession to the effect that he had engaged in anti-party and anti-government activities. Krivoruchko was a magnificent athlete, a man of unusual physical strength. He disarmed and beat up the interrogator in his own office. The guards on duty who rushed in to the interrogator's aid reduced Krivoruchko to such a condition that despite his iron constitution he died from his beatings.

I remembered the remark which had been made quite

recently by an officer of my acquaintance, a young communist: "The enemies of the people are not the ones arrested; they're the ones who are doing the arresting." *(Sazhayut ne vragov naroda, a vragi naroda.)* He was denounced, and arrested. His trial was expected to take place any day. He would be shot, of course.

The prisoner's story did more to me than simply recall memories in my mind. It provoked a line of thinking which, if my thoughts could have been read, would have caused my immediate arrest. I lay there, turning it all over in my mind. It was almost morning when I finally lost myself in sleep.

* * *

The guard brought her to me again on the following day. This time I sent him away without any prompting from my conversational partner. She greeted me as if I were an old acquaintance. She was more confident now, and her disposition was notably better than it had been the day before.

"You know," she began, "I have a rather guilty feeling that I am taking up too much of your time with my tale. No doubt it's quite dull for you to listen to all these details, and you are indulging me only out of courtesy and tact. But today I shall get to the most important part."

"Not at all," I answered, "I find your story very interesting, and I am glad to listen to you. And as for your feeling that I am listening to you out of tact," I laughed, "you are quite mistaken. I am an officer of the NKVD, and you are a prisoner. How can there be any question of tact between us? How could I be induced out of tact toward a prisoner to do something I didn't want to do? Do you remember how the guard treated you yesterday? And yet you speak to me of tact and courtesy."

She looked at me with surprise and a suggestion of reproach. "Why, what kind of a comparison are you making? That was a crude animal, a beast capable of snarling and shooting people, and nothing more. You can't expect anything more from such a creature. They don't think, they have no feelings."

I remonstrated. "A crude animal, you say? Doesn't think, has no feelings? You're mistaken. Outward appearances and actions don't always express the true feelings of a person. The demands of duty, discipline, training, that's one thing, but the true feelings, the unexpressed thoughts, can be quite a different matter. You know, this afternoon I met that soldier who handled you roughly and wanted to shoot you. I asked him, 'You're quite a hero, aren't you? You're pretty good at making war with women.' Do you know what he said? I'll repeat it for you word for word. Perhaps you'll be able to see through his crude speech to the basic goodness inside. He answered me like this: 'Why, what do you mean? Disobedience of the guards—that's a serious matter. You yourself would have been the first to demand firm measures, if I hadn't taken them.' Then he thought a bit, and added, 'It's a pity though. She's a good-looking babe. She's not used to riding in prison trains, I guess. What do you think she's in here for? What kind of a crime could she have committed?' That's your crude, unthinking animal for you. And there's logic for you. Actions don't always reveal the feelings."

"Did he really say that? It shows a fine, honest character.

So he had a warm heart after all. He was able to understand me. But why did he push me so rudely? What a terrible face he had!"

"Would you really have listened to him if he had politely requested you with a gallant smile to return to your place in line?"

"You're right, I wouldn't have paid any attention to him," she frankly answered, and then immediately asked, "But tell me, could he really have shot me?"

"Yes," I answered. "Under slightly different circumstances he not only could have shot you, but would have been obliged to do so. And he would have shot you regardless of the fact that you seemed good, and pretty, and that he was sorry for you. He would have shot you even though he sincerely doubted that you could have committed any crime. We have touched here on a very difficult psychological question," I said, and asked her to continue her story. She began where she had left off the day before.

"Very shortly after I moved with my children into the small room I ran out of money. I didn't have anything to live on. I tried to get a job. I thought it wouldn't be too difficult. You see, I know French, German and English quite well, and I used to spend a lot of time doing translations of scientific works for my father. But I was a relative of enemies of the people. I couldn't obtain a position anywhere. I was afraid to bring danger to former friends and acquaintances who had not yet been arrested, and so I refrained from contacting them for help.

"Before long I received another notice to appear at the NKVD. When I arrived, they brought me to the same Chekist who had interrogated me the first time. He was very pleasant and polite to me, and told me that he had good news. He said there was some hope that things would take a turn for the better. He promised me that in a few days he would arrange a meeting for me with my husband and my father. He said that he believed in the innocence of my loved ones. I eagerly began to try to prove to him that they could not possibly be guilty of anything, but he interrupted me, saying, 'I know, I know even better than you do, but for certain reasons we have to hold your father and your husband under arrest for a while yet, and even under rather unpleasant conditions.' He seemed to be so good, kind and sympathetic, that I immediately placed my full confidence in him.

"Then he explained to me that my husband and my father, without being aware of it themselves, were under the influence of the enemies of the people–participants in a counterrevolutionary anti-Soviet, anti-Party conspiracy. Formally they were not members of the group, and did not even know it existed, but they were victims of their credulity. Enemies of the people had made use of their names, positions and authority in order to further their own criminal deeds. His words were so convincing, he spoke with such sympathy, that I could not doubt his honesty. I believed him. He told me he was ready to do everything possible to help my husband and my father, that he hoped soon to have them released, and restored to their former positions. He expressed confidence that this would come to pass in the very near future.

"I could hardly believe what I heard. I was beside myself with joy. And yet, how could it be otherwise? He continued in his friendly, soothing voice, 'However, I shall need your help. We shall have to rehabilitate them, and establish their innocence. You will have to help me free the innocent. You must help me prevent the shooting of innocent people.'

"I eagerly told him that I was ready to do everything he wanted. With a kind, good-natured smile he said to me, 'Good, I see that you're an intelligent woman, that you love your husband and your father. We'll work together, you and I, to have them released.'

" 'But what must I do?' I asked him.

" 'For the time being, not a thing,' he replied. He told me that he would try to have things made more comfortable for my husband and for my father. He said that in three days I would be allowed a visit with them.

"I flew home as if on wings, and was ready to jump and shout with joy like a little girl. I wanted to stop every passer-by on the street and tell him about my good fortune. I told the children that papa and grandpa would soon be with us again, and that we would move back to our old apartment and live as we used to. O God, what ecstatic moments of hope and faith those were!

"The three days seemed to me an eternity. But finally, on the appointed day I went back to the NKVD, and was received by the kind, understanding investigator. Once again he greeted me warmly. Then he told me with a smile that the interview had been arranged. A guard led me through the long corridor. We went down in an elevator, then along some more corridors, and finally down some stairs. And then suddenly I was in a large room without windows, brightly illuminated by electric light. Along the wall was a long wooden bench, and by the opposite wall some chairs. My guide pointed to a place on the bench. I sat down. He went up to one of the several small doors to this strange room, pressed a buzzer, and silently seated himself on a chair opposite me. My heart pounded, and my head spun from excitement. One of the doors opened, and my husband came into the room. He had become thin, he was pale, and had a heavy growth of beard. With tears I threw myself around his neck. When I finally tore myself from him I saw my poor old father standing near us. I have no idea what I said, and I don't remember a thing that my father said to me. I can remember only that my husband told me that of late, for three days already, they had been taken out of solitary confinement and put into a cell together, that their food had improved, and that they were even receiving tobacco.

"For my part I assured them that they would soon be released, that I had been promised this, that the NKVD knew of their innocence. My husband comforted me and expressed hope that all would end well. My father said nothing. It seemed to me that only a few minutes had passed, when the guard told us that an hour's time had elasped, and that the visit was at an end. We said good-by to each other, and they were led away.

"On the way back I kept thinking about what my husband had told me, 'It was three days ago that they moved us into the same cell together, improved the food, started to give us tobacco.' It had all happened just as the investigator had promised me. He had promised to have my husband and my father freed, and he would do this, too. I walked quickly back along the corridors, hurrying as fast as I could, to talk again with this influential Chekist whom God had sent me in order to save my husband, my father, my children and myself.

" 'Well, now you've seen each other,' he said to me when I came into his office again. 'Don't worry, soon things will be good again, and we'll all have a celebration. And now, let's get on to our business.'

"I paid close attention to what he was saying. In my mind there was only one thought. 'I'll do anything, anything, so long as they are freed, and we can be together again.' He spoke slowly, distinctly, in a tone that left no room for misunderstanding:

" 'Yours is a good family, a well-known one. You have a large group of friends, both among Party people and in academic circles. They trust you and think highly of you. You are completely beyond suspicion. I am quite aware that at present you have no money, and that you and your children don't even have enough to eat. We shall take care of your material needs, and you will not suffer. Nobody must know of the help you are receiving, nor of our secret alliance. In order not to cause suspicion we'll get you some kind of a job. You must renew contacts with your former friends. You must win confidence, and engage those around you in conversations of a specific nature. Report to me the complete details of everything you hear.' He continued in this vein.

"It was only later, when I had already gotten home, that I realized what he had proposed to me, and to what I had given my consent. I experienced pangs of conscience, fear and a heaviness in my heart, as if I had done something terribly wrong. This feeling was deeply suppressed within me, however. The conviction that it was all necessary for the liberation of my loved ones stifled everything else in me.

"I had been recruited as a secret informer. Nobody would suspect me, the wife and daughter of 'enemies of the people,' as an agent of the secret police, an informer and provocateur. I would appear to everyone simply as an unhappy victim of the purge. I began to work. I met my chief every week, each time at a different meeting place appointed by him. I would report to him in detail where I had been, what I had heard, and who had said it. Some of the things I told him he demanded that I put in writing. At each meeting he would give me new assignments.

"Whenever I asked him whether I would be permitted another visit with my loved ones he answered that it was not possible for the time being. Suspicion would be aroused by the fact that an exception was being made in my case, while other relatives were being denied the privilege of visits. He regularly brought me letters however, and received those which I gave him. My husband and my father wrote in their letters that conditions had become quite good for them, that they had need of nothing, and that I should not worry. They wrote that they had high hopes of their early release.

"Meanwhile, I continued to operate. I took up again the former ties with the old acquaintances and friends I had known through my father and my husband. I enjoyed their full trust, and they did not hesitate to speak in my presence about matters which they would never have mentioned before strangers. And I of course reported everything I heard from them.

"My chief regularly gave me 300 rubles each month. In addition I had obtained a job as an embroideress in a sewing factory, where I also received about 300 rubles a month. This money was sufficient for a modest life with the children. My chief told me that he refrained from giving me more money only because he was afraid of arousing suspicion among my associates. 'Money betrays the secret!' he used to say.

"Several months passed in this manner. The assignments which my chief gave me were ever more and more serious ones. It had come to the point where he did not limit himself to requiring reports from me as to what people said and with whom they associated. He had me work up acquaintances with certain people who were of interest to him. I was to gain their confidence, establish relationships, and report on them. I did everything he required of me.

"On several occasions he took me to his office in the Lubyanka, and made me sign protocols of some kind. He never allowed me to read them, but would simply tell me briefly what was written in them. Sometimes he would bring some detail specifically to my attention. 'Don't forget this,' he would say. 'Be sure to remember this well.' 'You heard this from so and so, at such and such a time.' At first I used to offer a kind of feeble resistance to saying something which was not actually true; I recoiled from giving false testimony. Whenever this happened he would rudely shout at me and threaten me, that my husband and my father 'would be shot as mad dogs and enemies of the people!' In the end I always humbly agreed, and signed everything that he had demanded of me. He had stopped being polite and courteous with me. He was usually unceremonious, rude and demanding.

"One day he brought me to the Lubyanka and arranged a face-to-face confrontation between myself and one of my husband's old friends and colleagues. Before this confrontation he indicated to me what questions would be put to me, and what answers I would be required to make. He warned me that if I did not fulfill his demands, it would be very injurious to my husband's chances. I acquiesced. At the confrontation I was burning with shame. The prisoner was an old friend; I couldn't look him in the eye. But I said everything that was required of me. I signed their false evidence, and swore that I was speaking the pure truth, under penalty of answering before a court myself, should my testimony not be true.

"After the confrontation my chief was in very good spirits. He laughed a good deal, and praised me. He called me an iron Chekist. When I blushed from shame he said it became my good looks. I choked back the sobs born of insult, shame, and my powerlessness to resist.

"I had confrontations with other prisoners, also. One of them was a completely honest man with whom I had become acquainted after the arrest of my husband and of my father. I had been welcomed into his home as if I had been a member of his family. On the basis of my reports he had been arrested. I gave testimony against him exactly as my chief directed. When I was forced to confront him I almost fainted, but I played my role firmly. I had to use my last reserves of strength to summon the courage to do the base things which he demanded of me.

"One time my chief, as if by accident, introduced me into the society of some high ranking Chekists. He made me acquainted with one of them, one of his own superiors. He told me to become intimate with him. I fulfilled even this repulsive task.

"I stopped working at the factory. I had all the money I needed. I moved into a fine new apartment which my lover procured for me. The days of poverty had been left behind. Sorrow, however, was still my inseparable companion. I began to spend entire nights in the boisterous company of my lover and of others like him, important Chekists and their mistresses. I participated in prearranged nocturnal drinking sprees and orgies. I reported to my chief everything I saw, trying to remember every word said, and everything which happened during these wild nights.

"One of the friends of my lover tried to flirt with me and gain my favor. He was as disgusting to me as the other. One time this new admirer of mine came to my home in a drunken state. The children were asleep. There, alone with me, he told me about my lover—his friend. He revealed to me many of his personal and official secrets, as well as the offenses he had committed. He assured me that the man would soon be arrested, and that I might experience some unpleasantness as a result of my connection with him. He offered me his friendship.

"I was finding out at first hand what terrible things these people were doing, this celebrated, all-powerful NKVD and its leaders. I reported what my admirer had told me, to my chief. He was very pleased with me.

"No one ever doubted me. Not a soul suspected me of the terrible things I was doing. I don't know how it would have ended, this vulgar liaison of mine with this important Chekist, whom my chief had assigned to me as a lover against my will, if he had not been shortly arrested. My chief immediately received the position of the arrested man. It was a great promotion for him. He did not dispense with my services, however. He continued to direct my activities personally. The other Chekist who was attracted to me did not cease his attempts to become intimate with me. One time he came to me at home and tried to persuade me to come to his apartment. I refused. He gave me his telephone number and told me to turn to him if I were ever in trouble. At the time I didn't think that I would ever make use of his offer.

"The months passed. I continued to be an informer, provocateur and betrayer for my chief. I was able to console myself only by the knowledge that what I was doing was for the sake of my husband and my father. I noticed that of late my chief had once again changed his manner with me for the better. He dropped his rude ways, and once again showed me his attention. He became gracious and polite again. Then one time during our regular business meeting he invited me to a restaurant for dinner. There he proposed for the first time that I visit his bachelor apartment. I could not refuse him, since I was completely dependent upon him. The fate of my loved ones lay in his hands. I agreed. After that I began to visit him often at his place. The same kind of nocturnal orgies took place as before; only the participants were different.

"One time we were alone in his apartment. He was quite drunk. He proposed that I move in with him permanently. I was horrified. 'But what about my husband?' I asked with fear.

"On his drunken face, distorted with annoyance and anger appeared a repulsive grimace. He made a gesture with his hand that told me everything. 'They're already . . .' He caught himself, and fell silent.

"I knew immediately what he had been about to say. In a burst of despair I seized him and started shaking him with all my strength. I demanded that he finish what he had been about to say. I awaited his answer with terror. He burst into loud laughter. I was intoxicated too; I threw myself on the divan and broke into hysterical sobbing. Trying to quiet me, he began to say in his drunken voice, trying to reconcile me, 'That was just a stupid joke of mine. Everything's all right. I didn't think you loved him any more. Come on now, take it easy. Let's have a drink.'

"I drank more than usual that night. After a while the terrifying thought came to my mind for the first time, 'And what if my husband were to return? How could I look him in the face after everything that has happened?' I suddenly realized that the thing I was most afraid of, was that my husband might return. My head was reeling and buzzing from the wine which I had drunk. There were moments of consciousness, and then stupor again. But this terrible thought kept coming back, too: 'Perhaps it would be better that they never come back!' Again the buzzing in my head—another goblet of wine. That's how I passed that terrible night.

"I was brought home in the morning in an automobile. I awoke in the afternoon with a terrible headache. My first thought was about the incompleted phrase of yesterday. I made up my mind. I telephoned the Chekist who had offered me his services. I told him that I wanted to see him immediately.

"We were sitting in his luxuriously furnished apartment and drinking wine. He was repulsive to me, but I tried to be sweet and coquettish with him. Bracing myself, I asked him, 'Tell me sweetheart—you love me, I know—I want to be free. When did they shoot my husband?' He pressed me in his embrace, but I repeated, 'Answer me, tell me, that's all.' I trembled with fear, waiting for his answer. 'Six months ago,' he said, 'along with your father.' And then, as if having fulfilled his duty with this one phrase, he forgot about it. He began to speak tender words to me, and to caress me.

"With terror and disgust I pushed him away. I was wild with despair. I ran out into the street. I have no idea how I got home. The realization of the truth was such a shock to me that I was ready to end it all. Only the thought of the children restrained me. I had been deceived, insulted and used in the basest manner by vicious men. I despised myself for all that I had done.

"My chief called me up several times; he sent for me, but I refused to go to him. After a week of this he himself came to me one evening. We had a discussion. I told him that I was breaking off all contact with him. At first he tried to persuade me, and when I didn't react, he began to threaten. He told me that I had no right to give up my work in the state security service. Secrets had been entrusted to me, he said. I knew too much. I couldn't be left alone, or even at liberty. I was unshakable however; my sorrow and despair had given me new strength. I didn't care what they did to me. He drove off in a fury, after telling me, 'You'll regret this day!'

"Shortly thereafter, one day, I received an official notice to appear at the NKVD. I didn't go. A few days after that, they came one night and took me away. I cried, I screamed; I fought them off. The children wailed and clung to me. But they took me away.

"It was not until three months later, already late autumn, that they brought me up for interrogation. They charged me with having participated in an anti-Soviet counterrevolutionary organization, of having plotted to overthrow the government. As evidence of my guilt they brought up those connections with the arrested and executed persons which I had established on orders of my chief. The confrontations in which I had participated, as well as my conversance with the matters concerning which I had given testimony, all on assignment of my chief, served as further evidence of my guilt.

"I attempted to establish my innocence by all means. I told the investigator that I had simply fulfilled the assignments of a certain important Chekist, that I had been his secret agent. This admission of mine served as the basis for a new and even more serious charge against me. 'He was an enemy of the people,' I was told. 'He has already been shot, and you are a collaborator in his criminal activities.' And finally, they accused me of being the wife and the daughter of executed enemies of the people.

"Soon after the first interrogation they called me out of my cell again and announced that by decree of a Special Session I had been sentenced to ten years imprisonment and confiscation of all my possessions. The calmness and indifference with which I heard the sentence surprised even myself. I asked about the children. I was told that they would be sent to an orphan home, and would be brought up and educated as honest Soviet citizens, devoted to the Party. I was told it would be better for them not to know of the criminal acts of their parents.

"Shortly after that I was transferred to the exile transfer prison, where I awaited shipment to the camp. A week ago they loaded us into a convoy train, and brought us here."

The prisoner had finished her terrible story. She sat there in a state of complete exhaustion, holding her head in her hands. She remained motionless in this position for several seconds. Finally she raised her head, and got up from the chair. Her eyes were full of tears. She pressed her hands together in a gesture of supplication. Turning to me, she asked, "Tell me, am I really guilty? Did I really commit a crime? What did they sentence me for? What am I to do now?" She stood there in silence, with her despairing gaze full upon me, pleading with her eyes for my answer.

I sat looking at her in silence for several moments. My eyes were fixed on her face. She had evoked in me such a deep feeling of loathing, that whatever pity and sympathy I had felt for her at the beginning was smothered completely. Finally I said, "And after everything you've done, you consider yourself innocent? You feel that you have committed no crime?"

At first she did not comprehend the meaning of my words. Her wide open eyes remained fixed on my face. Then suddenly her face turned deathly white, and began slowly, slowly to draw itself out. Her lips began to tremble. Her lower jaw began to twitch convulsively. She seized her head in her hands. Her eyes took on an insane look, and then, as if only now for the first time she comprehended that which had for so long been buried in her subconscious mind, she gave a shrill, hysterical shriek. Then she fainted, and fell on the floor.

Upon hearing her shriek the guard who had been waiting in the next room ran into the office. I was standing behind the desk. I wasn't feeling well. I picked up the telephone and called for a doctor and aid men. The guard and I picked her up and laid her on the divan. She remained unconscious. Presently the medical personnel came and took her away on a stretcher to the dispensary.

FAMILY MEMBERS OF THE TRAITORS TO THE HOMELAND

FROM 1937 to 1939 great purges swept over the Soviet Union. Hundreds of thousands of people throughout the land, coming from all levels of society, were arrested by the organs of state security. The arrests began with members of the Politburo, high government officials and Soviet marshals, and wound up with ordinary white collar workers, laborers and peasants. They were arrested without regard to any former services which they had rendered to the Revolution or to the Party, and were exiled for long years in the camps as traitors to the homeland. Thousands were put in prison or shot as enemies of the people. Hundreds of thousands were dismissed from government service. Strict limitations were established as to the work which these latter might perform. They were deprived of the right to occupy any post of responsibility whatsoever, no matter where it might be, regardless of their professional qualifications. Well-known specialists, important party and government workers, high ranking officers, among them generals, were dismissed from service in disgrace. They were forced to obtain work as janitors, common laborers, watchmen, or if they were fortunate, as common clerks in some insignificant civilian administration, at a wage which did not even suffice for the nourishment of their families.

At that time it was difficult to find a family in the Soviet Union in which there had not been repressions of at least one of its relatives or close acquaintances. In the case of the highest government officials who were shot, the repressions extended to the members of their families as well. In 1937, a law concerning "Family Members of Traitors to the Homeland" was enacted. This law provided for the confinement of these persons in special camps for terms of eight to ten years. They were known by a special expression, which came to be part of the official juridical terminology in the Soviet Union at that time. The expression was "ChSIR," and was formed from the initial letters[1] of the official designation.

All persons whose fathers, sons or brothers had been shot during the purges were classified as ChSIR's. They were not brought before a formal court; their fate was decided by a special commission in absentia. They were arrested without warning and sent off to specially isolated camps. The length of their sentences depended on the former rank, authority and popularity of the head of the family. The more significant he had been, the longer was the term of imprisonment on the members of his family.

These special prisoners were kept in strict isolation, without the right of correspondence or visitors. No information was released concerning them, and it was absolutely impossible to ascertain what had happened to them after their arrest, or where they were located. They were handled as

[1] Chleny Sem'i Izmennika Rodiny—Family Members of a Traitor to the Homeland.

especially dangerous criminals, as "counterrevolutionaries."

Special camps for ChSIR's were established in various places in the Soviet Union, where they could be completely isolated, kept from all contact either with the local population or with other categories of prisoners. The administrative personnel and the military guard in such camps were selected with special care from the standpoint of political-moral reliability and devotion to the Party and the state.

In northern Kazakhstan is the city of Akmolinsk. About twenty kilometers from the city, in the open steppe, far from any inhabited point, one of these special camps was established. It had been constructed to accommodate a modest number of prisoners, by Soviet standards. There were only ten thousand persons confined in it. They were all women, relatives of "enemies of the people" and "traitors to the Homeland" who had been executed.

* * *

I was on my way to visit this special camp near Akmolinsk. I was curious about the place, having already heard a great deal about it. It was strictly forbidden for anyone to visit the camp, and likewise it was forbidden for persons of the administration, or the guard, to leave, except for a strictly limited number of the higher staff, and they only in exceptional circumstances, on official business. Furloughs and leaves of absence were not granted.

I had heard that the wives and other female relatives of many former high officials were confined there, for example Marshals Tukachevsky, Bluecher and Egorov; People's Commissar for Internal Affairs Yagoda, his deputies Prokof'ev, Berman, Frinovsky; and other highly placed Party, government, military and Chekist officials, who had been declared enemies of the people and shot during the great purge.

The strict isolation and the special secrecy prevailing in the camp had increased my curiosity even more. It was with great interest, therefore, that I travelled out there the very first time I was ordered to do so. From the Akmolinsk station to the camp it was about a twenty kilometer ride on horseback. I was still several kilometers from the camp when I perceived a group of women prisoners at work on the preparation of a kind of adobe. In central Asia this mixture of clay and rotten straw, dried out in the form of bricks, is called *saman*. It is used for the construction of houses and other buildings. The preparation of *saman* is hard work, demanding great physical exertion.

The group of prisoners consisted of about two hundred women. The entire area in which they were working was surrounded by armed soldiers of the guard, standing at intervals of one hundred meters. I stopped on the road and approached the scene of the work. The prisoners were broken down into several groups. One of these groups was digging out clay with shovels, and loading it onto wheelbarrows. Another group was trundling the loaded wheelbarrows to the point where the *saman* was being prepared; others were cutting the rotten straw with primitive hand chopping-knives and mixing it with the clay and the water; some were shaping the bricks by means of forms, and the rest were carrying the freshly formed *saman* on stretchers and laying it out on the *steppe* in a checkerboard pattern to dry. From time to time a column of from twenty to thirty ox-carts came up, under reinforced guard. The finished dried *saman* was loaded onto all the carts simultaneously, and the column would move off toward the camp under armed convoy.

Not one prisoner could leave the guarded work area, not one outsider could approach. The guard policed the area thoroughly each evening after the prisoners were led away, to make certain that no one left behind notes or any kind of article. They also had to make sure that during the night no one had secreted anything there for the prisoners. Every day, before the prisoners began to work, and each evening after they left, soldiers with dogs came up to the area, and a search was conducted. The dogs were specially trained for searching terrain. They could detect any foreign scent in the area, and find any strange articles, however small.

Merely by looking at the prisoners was it possible to distinguish without difficulty between the women who, unused to physical labor, were straining clumsily and taxing their strength to perform the heavy work, and those who had been accustomed to hard labor from a life spent at farm work, or who had come from workers' families. Almost all the women either worked barefoot or in large canvas shoes with wooden soles. They wore crude canvas trousers, dirty, patched in many places, often torn, and shirts of the same material and in the same condition.

The women were broken down into work brigades of from fifteen to twenty persons. The brigadiers did not perform labor themselves, but simply supervised the work of their brigades. They urged them on, and saw to it that no one stood about idly, or became distracted from the work in any way. The brigadiers performed their functions very conscientiously. They knew that if they performed poorly they might be removed from their favored positions, lose their privileges and be transferred to the ranks of the ordinary prisoners.

On each separate phase of the work there were tallyers, also prisoners. They checked off the work of each brigade as a group. The work of each individual prisoner was personally reckoned by the brigadier. There were boards on wooden supports, on which was noted in chalk the degree of fulfillment of the quotas of each brigade, as well as the progress toward fulfillment of the "socialist competition" contracts between brigades and between individual prisoners. Here stood the so-called "expediters," also prisoners. Their responsibility was to organize "socialist competition" between individual brigades, and between one prisoner and another. These "expediters" were also freed from the heavy labor.

The entire operation was under direction of a "work superintendent." She was the main figure on the project. Upon her lay all responsibility for organization of the work, as well as the meeting of the production quotas. The "work superintendent," the "instructors," the tallyers, as well as the brigadiers in the camp, were regarded as members of the lower administration of the camp, and as a matter of fact they all displayed a special zeal and severity in their relationship with the ordinary prisoners. They cherished the privileges and advantages which accrued to them in their positions of authority, and took care not to jeopardize them. This fact ensured that they support above all else the production programs, the discipline and the established regime of the camp.

The ordinary workers, too, urged one another on. They furiously scolded those who worked haplessly, who were lazy or who allowed their attention to wander from the work. There had been a time when I used to be amazed by this zeal of the prisoners, and by their mutual goading of each other to greater performance. In the Soviet lexicon this remarkable phenomenon is known by the terms "worker enthusiasm," "socialist organization of labor," "conscientiousness." Actually, of course, it owes its existence not to enthusiasm, but to something much more basic. The secret is explained quite simply. Each brigade receives a daily quota of work to be performed. If this quota is not met, the entire brigade receives a reduced ration on the following day. Instead of the regular twice-daily half liter of soup—made of herring, without any fat whatsoever, or simply out of sauerkraut with a half-rotten potato—they would receive this soup only once a day. The bread ration would also be reduced. Sometimes if the brigade did not meet its daily quota, it would be made to work beyond the usual ten-hour day in order to make up the shortage.

On the other hand, if a brigade over-fulfilled the quota within the ten-hour working day, then on the following day it would receive increased rations—the same soup, twice a day, but three quarters of a liter instead of a half. Brigades which consistently over-fulfilled the quotas would receive an increase of one hundred or two hundred grams in the bread ration.

This then, was the driving force in the Soviet camps. The people overtaxed their strength in order to get the extra half-liter of soup, smelling like slops, nicknamed "*balanda.*" This was what made the prisoners mercilessly goad each other on, for in each brigade, all answered for the performance of one, and one for all. Despite all this energy and the frequent over-fulfillment of the quotas however, the labor productivity remained generally at an extremely low level, due to the physical weakness of the prisoners. In a great many cases the prisoners, finally reaching the point of collapse, and despairing of ever meeting the quotas, would become completely indifferent. The slave-like conditions of the work produced a slave-like attitude toward it.

It would sometimes happen in the camps that the "work superintendents," seeing the exhaustion of the prisoners, would intentionally lower the quotas. Sometimes the tally-ers would mark down extra scores in favor of the prisoners, to help them out. By doing so they placed themselves in danger of suffering grave consequences. If discovered, they could expect at the very best to be removed from their posts in the lower camp administration and put to common heavy labor. More frequently in such cases these tender-hearted prisoner-supervisors would be accused of sabotage, of subverting the production system. They would be found guilty of "economic counterrevolution." For this crime the term of imprisonment could be increased by many years. Some offenders were sentenced to be shot.

Perpetual hunger played the dominant role in the con-scientiousness of all the prisoners. The central thought in every mind, the driving force, was bread. Hunger gov-erned the thoughts and regulated the conduct of the pris-oners, so that as long as they were able to think somewhat rationally, and so long as they were still able to work after a fashion—until they were reduced to complete exhaustion and despair. . . .

Not very long ago, here in western Europe, I happened to meet an American who had just arrived from the United States. He was a representative of an American motion-picture studio and was gathering material on Soviet camps for the production of a film. In conversation with me on the subject, he expressed complete bewilderment. "I simply cannot understand," he said, "why in the Soviet camps they keep the prisoners in such a state of hunger. Certainly if they were fed better, they would work more efficiently. I have been trying to find an answer to this question, to discover the reason, but I am at a complete loss."

I answered him in a half-jesting manner. I offered the opinion that if the prisoners in the Soviet camps were well-fed, then everybody in the Soviet Union would be competing to get into them, whereas under the present system everybody is afraid of them. My conversational partner burst out laughing. To my great disappointment he really took my answer for a joke. Naturally he was not satisfied. I sometimes wonder whether this inquisitive American ever finally received an answer to this question which was so interesting to him. . . .

"Here comes our 'General,' " said the chief of the escort to me, and indicated an approaching prisoner, tall, broad-shouldered and strongly-built. She was dressed exactly as all the other prisoners, but her uniform was not torn or soiled. Her shirt sleeves were rolled up to the elbows, and in her hands she was holding a large notebook. She walked with long strides and made energetic gestures. In a firm, deep-sounding voice she gave instructions to two women prisoners walking along beside her, who were also dressed better and were cleaner than the others.

"What do you mean, 'General'?" I asked the chief.

"That's what we call her here in the camp. She's the wife of the former commander of N Rifle Corps, who was shot as an enemy of the people. She's a serious and determined woman. They say that in the rifle corps they were more afraid of her than of her husband. Here in the camp the administration reckons with her. The prisoners are afraid of her, but they like her. She's very strict, but fair to everybody."

The "General" came up to us and dismissed the tallyers. She reported to me and stood still, in anticipation of any questions I might have. She appeared to be from forty-six to forty-eight years old. In her face, in her posture, in her movements and manners, was a resolution and dignity. One sensed a great internal strength in her, and inexhaustible energy and determination.

"Well, how's your work coming along?" I asked her, simply in order to have a topic of conversation. She took a step toward me, reported precisely and tersely, in a military manner, how many prisoners were at work, how many brigades, what kind of work, what the quotas were. She began to complain about the difficulties caused by the low qualifications of the worker force, and the poor physical condition of the prisoners.

"Fifty per cent of those who work with me are fine ladies. They've never had to work before. They were used to joy-riding around in automobiles. The only thing they're good for is manicures and *Kaffeeklatsches*. How can I meet the quotas with this kind of help? I can't get any production out of them. Shout at them a little bit, and they're ready to die on you. If you ride herd on them a little bit, to speed them up, they faint on you, and there's more work time lost. . . . If it weren't for the simple women to help the situation out, we wouldn't meet the quotas by even one half. They're used to heavy labor."

She's a tough one all right, I thought to myself. It's not hard to imagine what fear she can inspire in these fine lady prisoners of hers, as she calls them.

"But certainly," I said to her aloud, "you can't be much more used to physical labor than they are. I should think you would be able to sympathize with them. If I'm not mistaken, your husband was commander of the N Rifle Corps."

"Before I became the wife of the Corps Commander, I used to cut hay in my village; I milked cows and worked as hard as any man. I spent the entire Civil War at the front with my husband, marching at his side and fighting against the White generals. I possessed the "Red Banner" for distinguished service in battle. Before my arrest I was a delegate to the Supreme Soviet of the USSR. I was a party member in 1919. . . . I'm not one of their kind. They're pretty young things who jumped into comfortable marriages with People's Commissars. They're used to luxury; they don't know what life's all about. They got their position in life cheaply, and now here they are and can't get used to life with a shovel in their hands."

Her words were laden with bitterness and ill-will toward these "fine ladies," but still it could be sensed that she had a certain sympathy, or at least a kind of pity for them. But her deeper sympathies were evidently with the simple women of peasant and worker origin, to whom she was closer by social origin, and upon whom she depended to meet her production quotas.

My curiosity led me to ask her an impertinent question, one which touched her in a sensitive place. "May I ask what your husband was accused of?"

"Enemy of the people!" She answered me sharply and dryly. Anger at my curiosity flared up in her face, but she did not have the right to refuse to answer me. "With your permission, Citizen Chief, I must return to my work!" Without waiting for my answer she resolutely turned and took off with quick steps for the place where the prisoners were working, making comments and giving directions to the workers on the way.

From the point where the clay was being dug to the place where it was being kneaded, a distance of some two hundred meters, there was laid a narrow plankway. Along these planks wheelbarrows loaded with clay were being pushed. The empty wheelbarrows were rolled back to the clay pit directly on the ground. About thirty or forty women were at work with the wheelbarrows.

My attention was attracted to a young woman. She was clumsily and ineffectually straining with all her might to manage a heavily-loaded wheelbarrow. Considerable skill was required to negotiate the narrow plankway, in order to keep the wheel from skidding off to one side. It was evident that the woman was completely unable to handle her wheelbarrow. Immediately behind her, at intervals of two or three paces, followed similarly laden wheelbarrows, pushed by other prisoners. The woman who had attracted my attention was falling far behind those going on ahead of her. She was moving slowly, with great difficulty. The prisoners coming after her were shouting and goading her on. She was breathing heavily, and was becoming noticeably unnerved. She could not keep her wheelbarrow on the plankway; it repeatedly rolled off onto the ground. Each time she had difficulty getting it back on the narrow plank. This held up those who were following her. She was not very far from me when her wheelbarrow again rolled off the planks. This time the wheel became embedded in the soft ground. She did not have enough strength to move it. From behind her the shouts and abuse became more intense. The wheelbarrows crowded behind her and came to a stop—a kind of traffic jam. The woman was gasping for breath, weeping, straining herself to the utmost, but she was unable to move her wheelbarrow. Several other prisoners came up to her and with their combined strength put it back on the planks, while she stood helplessly by, weeping, wiping her perspiring face with her sleeve. Behind her the shouts and abuse were again heard: "What are you waiting for? Get a move on! Because of you we're not going to meet the quota. Let's go, Miss White Hands! There aren't any commissars to flirt with here!"

The woman, exerting all her strength, got the wheelbarrow rolling again. The others followed her. But before she had gone more than a few meters farther, her wheelbarrow rolled off the planks again, and as she clumsily attempted to right it, tipped over. A portion of the clay fell out on the ground. The procession came to a standstill once more. A brigadier ran up and with a curse exasperatedly turned the wheelbarrow completely upside down and to one side, freeing the way for the others. Once again the wheelbarrows began to roll rhythmically along the plankway.

The poor woman stood forlornly, with her hands at her sides, and wept helplessly. Then finally, after some prolonged and clumsy manipulations and with considerable strain she succeeded in setting her wheelbarrow right side up again. She began to scoop up clay from the ground with her hands. The prisoners pushing their wheelbarrows past her reacted in various ways to her misfortune. Some offered her advice and sympathy, although they did not dare to leave the work to help her. Others ridiculed her.

The "General" came up. With a few sharp stern words she cut off those who were laughing. She listened attentively to the explanation of the weeping woman, and then ordered her to come with her. From a distance I saw the "General" giving orders that another prisoner be put on the wheelbarrow, and that this one be put on another kind of work. I went to where the prisoner was working on her new job.

"Why did they put you to work with a wheelbarrow when you can't handle it?" I asked her.

"I've only been working here three days. The brigadiers on the common labor are very ill-disposed toward us intellectuals, first because we work poorly, and second because of our past. They simply don't like us, and they see to it that we are assigned to the heaviest work, to discipline us."

"But certainly the brigadiers have a past which is similar to your own. They're here in the camp for the same reason you are–because of their husbands. What difference can there be?"

"Why, all the difference in the world. They are simple women, of proletarian origin, as we are accustomed to say, and their husbands, because of whom they are serving time, did not have very important posts. That's why they hate us wives of important figures. They are especially ill-disposed toward intellectuals. They won't allow us on administrative work, on the pretext that we wouldn't be able to perform it satisfactorily. These simple women, despite the fact that their fate is identical with ours, dislike us intensely. They say that it was because of us that their husbands were shot. Now they are getting their revenge. They call us 'aristocrats,' and 'commissars.' They never forget our past."

"What post did your husband formerly hold?"

"My husband was Commander-in-Chief of the Far East Army–Marshal Bluecher. We lived in Khabarovsk."

"And what was the husband of your brigadier?"

"He was a chauffeur in Moscow, to Gamarnik, formerly Chief of the Political Administration of the Red Army."

"But are there really no other, easier jobs which you could perform?"

"Certainly there are. I used to work in the sewing shop. It was easier there. Then someone denounced me, and said that I was defending my husband, and claiming that he had been completely innocent. For that they put me on the very heaviest labor—on the clay. If it weren't for the 'General,' it probably would have been all up with me."

Not wishing to interrupt the rhythm of the work and distract the prisoner from her work by my conversations, I moved on. The chief of the convoy, who had been accompanying me all the time, said: "She keeps boasting that she was a marshal's wife. Here in the camp there are three wives of Bluecher like her. When they arrested them they all denied it, and said that they had no relationship to him. Now they quarrel among themselves; each one maintains that she was Bluecher's real wife, although each one has a different surname. This one was no wife of Bluecher—she was one of his mistresses. They put her in here for having relationships with an enemy of the people. . . ."

We went over to the place where the clay was being dug. At some distance from the workers an elderly woman was sitting idly by. I noted that one of her hands was bandaged in rags, and that she carefully supported it with her other hand. It turned out that she had lost her balance at work, and had fallen into a quarry and dislocated her arm. Now she was waiting for the transport which was supposed to come for the *saman*, in order to ride back with it to the camp.

I went up to her; she stood up. She was a small frail

woman about fifty-five years old. I inquired as to what had happened to her. I asked how long her sentence was and for what reason she had been sent to the camp.

"I am the sister of the President of the Supreme Soviet of the Ukraine Petrovsky; my name is Petrovskaya. He was shot as an enemy of the people, together with his son, who was a general. I was sentenced to ten years of strict isolation. I don't know what I was sent here for. I have never lived with them, and in more recent years, after my husband's death, we severed all contact whatsoever. Petrovsky lived in Kiev, and his son, my nephew, in Moscow. I lived in Dnepropetrovsk. My husband died several years ago. He was also an important party figure. We were personally acquainted with Vladimir Il'ich Lenin, and his wife Nadezhda Konstantinovna was a close friend of mine. What kind of enemies of the people can we be, we Petrovsky's? We belonged to the old Bolshevik guard, as 'Il'ich' used to call us.

"For the last two years, ever since I was put in here, I have been submitting complaints regularly. I have written several times to the Politburo, to Comrade Stalin, to the Supreme Soviet of the USSR and to People's Commissar for Internal Affairs Beria, but so far I haven't received an answer to a single one of the letters.

"You are evidently from the Center," she continued in a pleading voice. "I beg you, make inquiries, acquaint yourself with my case. I am a sick old woman. In the two years that I have been sitting in this camp I have become weak, I've become an invalid. What kind of a worker am I, especially for such heavy work? Can I really be of any use digging clay? Here today I fell, hurt myself, dislocated my arm. . . . And do you know why they put me to work on the *saman*? Up until a month ago I worked in the kitchen. Then, when I began to demand that I receive an answer to my complaints, I was reprimanded for it. I couldn't put up with that. I said that I intended to register a complaint about the local administration here. So then they put me on the heaviest penal labor. How can I survive here with my delicate health under such terrible conditions? Here even the young strong people become invalids in a short time. . . . I feel that I shan't live much longer. . . ." She began to weep quietly, silently, wiping with her dirty rags the tears which were running down her face.

* * *

I rode up to the camp itself. For the prisoners there was a row of low, one-story barracks built of *saman*, with flat clay roofs and small windows, whitewashed with lime. At some distance from these stood the administrative buildings and the stables, storehouses, kitchens, workshops and the like.

The camp was enclosed by two rows of barbed wire fence three meters high. Between the fences, standing at a distance of fifty meters one from the other, stood posts with electric lights on them, and at the corners and along the wire fence stood guard towers, mounted on which were small hand operated searchlights. Each tower was equipped with a field telephone. Around the outside wire fence went a ploughed strip of earth five or six meters in width. This was called the "control strip," and no one dared to set foot in it. Every day it was gone over with a raking device, in order that the surface would always be finely crumbled, and any footprint would be clearly discernible, be it that of a person, or even of a hare which might accidentally run across it. In wintertime the blanket of untouched snow made such ploughing unnecessary. Along this control strip went a narrow path, and every morning at dawn a guard patrol with search dogs would pass along it. Upon discovery of a human footprint in the control strip the dogs would take up the scent and the patrol would immediately pursue the runaway. On such an occasion a state of alert would be declared and a thorough personal count of the prisoners would be conducted. The guard would be put in a state of vigilance and reinforced, and an organized search operation would be mounted. The state of alert would continue until it could be determined who had entered the control strip and for what purpose. On all sides of the camp, at a distance of one hundred meters from the fence, on low posts, set in the ground at close intervals, were fastened plywood boards, with large signs in the Russian and the Kazakh languages: "HALT! KEEP AWAY. WILL SHOOT WITHOUT WARNING." On one side of the camp were gates and an entrance-booth, at which stood sentries with rifles.

A few dozen meters from the camp was located a small settlement, in which the officials of the camp administration and of the guard lived. The buildings of this settlement contrasted sharply with the buildings of the camp itself. They were little, detached houses consisting of one or two apartments each, with little gardens, each enclosed by walls made of *saman*. On the edge of the settlement was located a *kaserne* in which the guard force was billeted. A sentry was posted at the entrance.

It was not without reason that the installation was regarded as a camp of strict isolation for especially dangerous prisoners. Among these inmates were considerable numbers of relatives and friends of former very high government and party figures. They knew a great deal about matters which are diligently concealed by the Party and the government. In this lay their danger to the Communist regime.

Construction work was in progress not only in the camp itself, but in the administration buildings as well. New buildings were being constructed, and existing ones were being made larger. It was evident that the camp was being expanded.

As I was riding up I noted that on one of the towers a sentry was observing me. He evidently guessed from my uniform who I was. He picked up the field telephone, gave the handle a few rapid cranks, and spoke a few words. My arrival was being announced. A moment later I saw first one, then another figure in uniform, armed with pistols, come out of the entrance-booth, look attentively in my direction, and disappear again.

I came up to the gates. The sentries courteously but firmly detained me, and as if my appearance here had been unexpected by them, one of them pressed a signal button. Out of the booth came the duty officer and asked me who I was and what I wanted. When I identified myself, he came to attention and saluted me, but demanded that I produce my credentials. Checking my identification card, he carefully compared the photograph with my face, and then in addition examined my travel orders, which directed my trip to the Akmolinsk special camp for a period of temporary duty. After having gone through this formality the duty officer said to me, "You will pardon me, Comrade Chief, but according to my orders I must now call the Commandant. I shall have to ask you to wait here in the admission office until his arrival."

I acceded to his request, went into the booth, and sat down. I sensed that I was participating in the fulfillment of a special formality. I understood quite well that this formality was now being meticulously observed for my particular benefit, simply because I was a representative of the high command. They were trying to impress upon me the exemplary manner in which they performed their duty. Naturally, the entire guard force knew of my arrival, and was expecting me. This was quite clear. I knew very well that in accordance with long tradition there existed in the guard troops a secret warning system between commanders and their colleagues in other installations, advising of any impending visits from the higher command. These warnings are transmitted by post, by telegraph, by telephone, and if none of these methods is feasible, then they warn each other by couriers, and no matter how much secrecy is observed by an official concerning his travel to the troop units, he very rarely succeeds in arriving unexpected. In this particular case, horses had been sent to the station for me, so naturally they knew I was on my way, and the entire guard force had been appropriately instructed. I also knew that as early as the day before yesterday, in anticipation of my arrival in the Akmolinsk camp, everything had been gotten in order. They had selected the most efficient, energetic duty officers, and for my special benefit were observing all regulations most punctiliously. By their ritualistic observance of these rules they were emphasizing the alertness and mistrust of all persons, whoever they might be, which had been drilled into them.

The door opened, and the commander of the guard entered. He knew me well. He presented himself formally to me in a military manner, and excused himself for having made me wait.

* * *

Several days passed. I became acquainted with the chief of the camp, as well as with the chief of the local state security office. I passed the evenings in their homes as a guest. The camp commandant was an old cadre Chekist, who had been transferred from operational to administrative duties. Notwithstanding his many years of service in the state security organs, he had become almost completely uninterested in matters of an operational nature, and he devoted his entire attention to the purely administrative problems connected with the operations of this camp.

He informed me on all aspects of the camp's activities. He told me what tremendous technical difficulties were connected with the arrival of the first shipment of ChSIR's at the camp. There had been absolutely no accommodations, and the prisoners were obliged for several weeks to live under the open sky, enclosed by barbed wire. There were no kitchens; the food was cooked in kettles over open fires. There were no uniforms or work clothes. Even the tools necessary for construction work were insufficient to go around. It was necessary to launch emergency projects to make *saman*, to erect barracks, administrative buildings, storehouses, and the like. All this was done by the prisoners, the majority of whom were completely unaccustomed to physical labor, and who were absolutely unsuited for construction work.

By the onset of winter they had succeeded in hastily erecting barracks buildings. The bricks had not been completely dried however. With the frosts they became covered with ice, and in the spring fell apart, so that it was necessary to begin the construction all over again. There was insufficient coal for heating; there was not enough food, since the original supplies had not been calculated for so large a number of prisoners as were sent to the camp. As a result of these conditions many prisoners became exhausted, fell ill, became invalids. Many died.

The camp commandant told me that the labor of the ChSIR's had been utilized to construct twenty large barracks designed to accommodate five hundred persons each. They had built many other buildings as well, including a small group of houses for the administration. He said that the construction was still going on, but the general situation was much better now than it had been before. He told me that in addition to the construction projects and the preparation of building materials there were various other worker activities, including arts and craft shops, where the prisoners painted pictures, made sculptures, did delicate embroidery, made children's toys and other artistic articles which, as he expressed it, "would absolutely thrill" me.

He also explained to me with vexation however, that he did not have the authority to use the ChSIR's on any other type of work except common hard labor, that his instructions from Moscow explicitly and strictly forbid it. He told me that the Center's instructions concerning the handling of the ChSIR's prescribed particularly severe treatment for them. These instructions were so completely illogical, contradictory and unrelated to conditions in the camp however, that they simply were not observed. By taking advantage of their contradictions and lack of logic it was possible to justify this non-observance. He cited for me a few examples of these regulations:

> The ChSIR's are to be used only on common heavy labor, and are not to be utilized for office work, or permitted to work in their own specialties. Neither may they be permitted to serve as members of the lower camp administration.
>
> The ChSIR's are deprived of the right of correspondence. They may not receive visitors, and they may not submit applications or complaints. It is strictly forbidden to give out any information concerning them to any person. Should ChSIR's violate camp discipline, or refuse to work, they are to be brought before a court and punished by the severest means, up to and including the firing squad.

"Now you can see what nonsense it is," he said. "The instructions say, isolate them, and use them only for common heavy labor. Don't permit them on administrative work, or to work in their own specialty.

"As far as isolation is concerned, there's no problem. My camp is isolated, and well isolated. You yourself can see this. There is no other category of prisoners here, just ChSIR's, ten thousand of them. We need doctors, and aid personnel, and there aren't any, except from among the ChSIR's themselves. So what can I do? I take my specialists from wherever I can find them, regulations or no regulations. What choice do I have? I need technicians and builders. Where shall I get them from? I appoint them from among the ChSIR's. I need work superintendents, brigadiers, tallyers, office workers, cooks, storekeepers, and all other sorts of specialists. Where in the world am I going to get them? Only from the ChSIR's, nowhere else.

"According to regulations not a single ChSIR may be

moved from place to place without an armed escort, even within the confines of the camp. Why, in order to comply with an order like this I would have to have a guard regiment of three thousand men. How could I possibly make out with the five hundred that I have at present? I simply ignore the regulation, that's all. If I were to observe it to the letter, I'd have to assign a guard with a rifle to every water-carrier, to every messenger from the office, to every prisoner who leaves the barracks to go to the latrine. How can I do it? I'd like to see how the ones who wrote these regulations would carry them out, if they were in my place. It would be interesting to see how they'd solve these problems.

"Of course, when you violate one rule, you have to break another, and then another and another. It's the only thing I can do. I've sent several reports about all this to Moscow. They agree with my reasoning, express sympathy, but they won't authorize me to deviate from my instructions. 'Do it on your own responsibility, if you want to,' they say, 'but we can't authorize you to do it—these are strict orders from the Party Central Committee. The regulations are going to be changed in the near future,' they say. Well, I've been waiting for two years now, and I haven't seen any changes yet.

"So you see, circumstances simply force me to violate the orders of the Center deliberately. So far everything has turned out all right, but if anything serious should happen—I couldn't possibly escape facing a court for infractions of regulations, and connivance with enemies of the people. But frankly, the fact that they are enemies of the people has worked to my advantage in a way, at least so far. Because of the strict isolation which has been ordered, and because of the fear that most people have concerning contact with the element which I have in my camp, it has been generally forbidden for any person to come here, even on official business. You're the first one who has been here in two years. But now I suppose there will be others. I'll have to expect trouble. . . ."

The camp commandant continued, "On my own authority and risk I have set up arts and crafts shops in the camp. You'll be astonished to see what they turn out in them!" He went into another room and returned in a moment with an exquisitely made Gobelin tapestry in the French style, and laid it on the table. "Look at this. Nine meters of silk at a cost of 450 Rubles, nine meters of lining at 480 Rubles, silk for embroidery, 500 skeins at 100 Rubles, three months work for an embroideress at ten hours a day—labor cost according to camp calculation, 198 Rubles. This Gobelin cost us 1000 Rubles. That's my salary for one week. . . . But look at the quality, the craftsmanship! Highly qualified specialists have told me that such a Gobelin would cost at least fifty thousand Rubles. And here we take such craftswomen as these, and put them to work with a shovel and a wheelbarrow. What for? It's all so stupid."

He began to show me portraits of the leaders embroidered in silk, and oil paintings, mosaic cigar boxes, jewel caskets, large album covers, and other superbly executed works of art. "I've sent many of these exquisite things as gifts to our high command in Moscow; I even sent one personally to the People's Commissar. They accept them, and thank me, but they never ask me where they came from, or who makes them. Last year I sent some of our artistic productions to the All-Union Exposition in Moscow. My artists had made a great number of exquisite things in the

Kazakh national style. They had spent several months on them. They received a great deal of praise, and won quite a few prizes. True, they had all been sent to the exposition as examples of 'Soviet art of the Kazakh people.' Naturally not a word was said about their having been made in the camp, but all the same it was pleasant for me—my participation in 'Soviet national art.'

"My local chief of state security matters at first protested against the violations I was permitting in the camp, and even made a complaint to Moscow about it, but now he himself has begun to overlook them. He has become convinced that it's unavoidable. And besides, he enjoys getting costly works of art for pennies. He too has sent quite a few of them to his high command through state security channels.

"There's only one great difficulty—there's not enough money to buy the material we need: linen, silk, paint, brushes and so forth. We can't include them in the budget estimate, because it isn't provided for in the plan, and we can't skim off too much from camp funds for such things. But we somehow figure out ways and means.

"Unfortunately a large percentage of the inmates here are weak, sick and invalids—generally unfit for work. And it's significant to note that their number is growing very rapidly. Two years ago, when they first started to send ChSIR's here, the weak and the sick comprised only about five per cent of our total, and now they constitute around thirty per cent. It's only natural—the population of our camp being made up ever more and more of the delicate element—that those who were spoiled in their life before they came here would meet such a fate. Generally speaking, it's a very inadequate work force."

I also had occasion to talk with the chief of the state security section. My conversation with him had an entirely different character. His opinions concerning the camp and the prisoners were at variance with those of the camp commandant. He was completely uninterested in the camp construction projects, as well as the handicraft shops (except for the products which were turned out there). The capacity of the worker force did not interest him, nor did the state of its health. All of this was outside his field of vision. He was a young officer, with little experience. He had completed the course of instruction at the central NKVD school only a year ago, but he was considered a firm, able and energetic Chekist.

"From the political and ideological standpoint there is a very difficult situation in our camp," he said to me. "A significant portion of the ChSIR's were formerly members of the families of important people, and they circulated in the highest governmental society. Ordinary citizens never came into contact with them. They lived a life entirely apart from that of ordinary citizens of the Soviet Union. . . . And now, here in the camp, they find themselves in a different situation. As a result of the fact that they are highly informed on many state questions, permitted only to a very limited number of our highest party officials, they can be very dangerous. Here at the camp they conduct conversations not only among themselves, but even with soldiers of the guard, which by their very nature constitute bare-faced counterrevolution. They slander the government and the Party. They think up all kinds of cock and bull stories which they pass off as the truth. We recognize this subversive talk for what it is, but sometimes the soldiers of the guard fall under the influence of these conversations. We strictly forbid the guard to converse with the ChSIR's, except for the minimum essential in line of duty. But how can you tie their tongues, how can you keep an eye on all the conversations which they carry on among themselves? The soldiers who are on escort duty with the prisoners on the work projects are among them every day for ten straight hours almost without control or supervision. The devil only knows what they say to each other.

"It's very difficult to set up informant nets among these ChSIR's—the majority don't want any part of informant work. As a result we don't have enough information about what's going on among the prisoners. As an example: you call up someone who seems a likely recruitment prospect. You start to talk to her; you try to create an incentive by offering her various privileges—tobacco, bread, and so forth. And what do you think? Either she bursts into tears and says that she can't do it, that she's afraid, or else she'll come up with some hysterical drivel like, 'It makes no difference if you die here. Do what you want. Go ahead and shoot me if you want to. I'm not going to inform on my friends.' You're already acquainted with the type, I know—rotten intelligentsia.

"Now of course, the criminal element, the bandits, the thieves, the prostitutes, the bribe-takers, the swindlers and so forth—these are people you can work with. You can build up a decent informant net with them inside a camp. This is the social element which is close to us. But here in this camp, you see, there isn't any such element. They're all counterrevolutionaries, these ChSIR's. It's very difficult to operate with them. But the thing which bothers us most of all is the anti-Soviet influence on the camp-personnel—on the guard, on the administrative employees.

"Last year the wife of a former People's Commissar, confined here, went into such a state of hysterics that it was quite embarrassing, especially since it took place in the presence of many other prisoners and the guard. In her fit she started to shout things which I simply can't repeat to you. She began to slander Comrade Stalin, and Comrade Poskrebyshev.[2] It was terrible! She'd picked up a lot of nonsense of all kinds from her husband and from other enemies of the people, and now in her hysteria she was screaming it out at the top of her voice. We had to tie her up and put her in solitary. Two days later, on orders from Moscow, I took her personally myself to the Central Isolator in Moscow. They shot her, of course.

"But do you have any idea," he went on, "of what kind of conversations go on among the soldiers and the officers of the guard? Here, I'll show you the latest operational summary." He took a heavy dossier out of his desk and began to leaf through it. When he found what he was looking for, he began to read aloud:

> Four officers of the guard: Kotor Vasily, Minaev Victor, Kuzmin Stepan, Fomin Dmitry, gathered together with their wives in the quarters of the last-named, and became drunk and disorderly. While in this condition they recounted matters which they had heard from the prisoners as follows:
>
> a. Toward the end of 1923, when Comrade Lenin was gravely ill and his condition was already hopeless, he allegedly called Comrade Stalin and begged him to give him poison to end his life. This conversation was allegedly overheard by the wife of Comrade Lenin, Nadezhda Konstantinovna Krupskaya, and she immediately reported this to the Politburo of the Central Committee of the Party. Measures were taken, and Lenin's suicide was prevented. It was this

[2] Member of the Politburo and chief of the personal secretariat and personal office of Stalin.

incident which gave rise to the saying in the Politburo of the Central Committee that 'Lenin knew where he had to go for poison.'

b. The mass repressions of the years from 1937 to 1939 were allegedly executed by order of Comrade Stalin for the elimination of all those inimically inclined toward himself.

c. The writer Maxim Gorky was poisoned allegedly at the order of Comrade Stalin, since in his last years he was critical of the regime. It was allegedly ordered that the literary archives of Gorky were all to be destroyed.

d. Former Marshals Egorov and Bluecher attempted to flee after the execution of former Marshal Tukachevsky!

e. Comrade Stalin allegedly ordered that his wife Alleluya be poisoned for criticizing his policies!

He broke off reading. "That's a sample," he said. "I have a whole collection of similar conversations, just like this one, on record here. Where does all this come from? Obviously it's all the result of this intimate association with enemies of the people here in the camp. Such counterrevolutionary agitation could be perpetrated only by enemies of the people, with deliberate premeditation. These aren't chance conversations. I am giving this matter my personal attention at present. There are six 'beauties' sitting here in my solitary right now—the wives of various riff-raff. I have definitely established that they were the ones who originated these conversations. In a few days I'll send them all to Central Isolator in Moscow. They'll take care of them there in short order."

I asked him whether he was quite certain that such conversations actually took place, whether he had considered the possibility of distorted information. He looked at me with surprise for a moment, and then burst out laughing. "That's impossible. We had a tested informant in this company—one of the officers. He's always given precise and valuable information. Many of his reports have been corroborated by other sources. I'm as sure of him as I am of myself."

He began to leaf through the dossier again, looking for something else to read to me. "Here's one more interesting incident I'll read to you," he said when he had located it.

> Platoon Commander, Party member Frolov, Nikolai, on the 16th of June at 1800 hours in a conversation with his soldiers in the kaserne told them what one of the ChSIR prisoners had told him concerning the wife of Marshal Budenny. Marshal Budenny's wife, a young and very beautiful woman, was having intimate relations with enemy of the people former Marshal Tukachevsky. After Tukachevsky's arrest Comrade Stalin summoned Marshal Budenny and informed him that his wife was to be arrested for having relations with an enemy of the people, but that he, Stalin, was aware of Marshal Budenny's honesty and devotion, and did not wish to compromise him. Comrade Stalin proposed to him that he personally turn his wife over to justice and reveal her liaison with Marshal Tukachevsky.
>
> Marshal Budenny immediately telephoned his home and told his wife that she was to prepare herself to accompany him to a state banquet in honor of some event or other. When Marshal Budenny arrived home his wife was already in evening dress. They entered an automobile, and Marshal Budenny himself took her to the Lubyanka and turned her over to the NKVD, denouncing her for her affair with an enemy of the people. She was shot.

"Well now, what do you think of it? Could you possibly invent a more stupid and dirty piece of gossip if you tried? I looked into this matter also. I meticulously investigated it myself. Utter and complete nonsense! And get this: Platoon Commander Frolov is a wonderful Party Comrade. Devoted and reliable. When he related this tale, he was enraptured over Marshal Budenny's act. 'What dedication!' he said. 'He didn't even spare his own wife!'

"Here you see a trustworthy comrade like Frolov, spreading the gossip manufactured by these females. We warned him; he immediately saw his mistake. It's just an example of the harm that can be caused by these conversations, and from naïve soldiers listening to them. We have strict regulations, of course, absolutely forbidding conversations with the ChSIR's. As a matter of fact, they are even forbidden to talk *about* the prisoners, even among themselves. But the regulations are flagrantly disregarded; the conversations continue. I suppose we'll have to bring some of them to trial for such conversations, much the same way as we try persons for divulging official secrets—just to set an example for the others.

"As for the officers whom I've just told you about, they don't know about it yet, but the dossier will soon be turned over to a military tribunal. Right now we're considering what should be done with their wives. We certainly can't permit them to remain at liberty, to wag their tongues all over the place. For two years now they have been seeing and hearing all kinds of nonsense and gossip like this. . . . They know more about what's going on here than their husbands do. It's quite a problem—what can we do with them? Perhaps the best solution will be to bring them before a court, too."

A bottle of wine had done much to loosen the tongue of this boastful young Chekist, so favorably regarded by his superiors as "energetic, capable and merciless toward enemies of the people." This conversation with him evoked in me an involuntary premonition of danger. I remembered the short conversations which I myself had had with the ChSIR's on the work projects upon my arrival at the camp a few days ago. A certain uneasiness crept up—had I perhaps said something wrong? Or had one of the prisoners said something improper to me? I resolved to be more careful, and to forget about my original intention to become closer acquainted with the ChSIR's and their life in this camp. But just the same, I wanted very much to visit the art shops, which the camp commandant had recommended as a most interesting sight.

* * *

On the eve of my departure the camp commandant took me around to "show me the sights of his domain." The chief of the state security went along with us, as well as the commander of the guard. The officer of the day was our escort.

The camp had comparatively few people in it—most of the prisoners were out on the work projects; only the sick prisoners, and those unfit for labor remained in the buildings. We were passing by a row of long barracks in which the prisoners were accommodated, and also past the infirmary, standing a short distance away. Suddenly a strange-looking female prisoner appeared before us from somewhere or other. She appeared to be about thirty-five or forty years old. Her gray hair was tousled, her eyes had an insane look; her movements were erratic. She was very much excited, was breathing heavily, and twitching all over. She came up to me, gripped my arm strongly with both hands and, convulsively pressing it, began to talk very rapidly.

"Ah, Comrade! You finally got here! How long I've been waiting for you! At last! I'm so happy!" She turned away from me and began to wave her arms. Addressing no one in particular, she enthusiastically exclaimed: "You see? I told you he'd send one of his people to me. . . . And here he is. Now we'll talk things over." She seized me then once more by the hand and continued looking me straight in the eyes. "Do pardon me, Comrade! But I simply don't know where I can receive you. Conditions are so abominable here—there's just no place where we can talk."

The camp commandant turned to the duty officer who was escorting us: "What the hell is this? Who let her out again? Get her back into the dispensary. She's crazy," he said to me in a loud voice.

"Oh no! It's you! You're the one who's crazy!" The prisoner threw herself upon him. "Bootlicker, liar, coward, fascist! Now I'm going to tell this comrade right now!" pointing to me with her hand, "so he'll make them put you in a straitjacket and stick you in the cold cell. . . . Now you can't do anything to me anymore. I can see what kind of a person this comrade is. He'll show you! He'll straighten things out around here!

"First of all, take down the barbed wire! Then get rid of the parrots with their candles.[3] And then take him, him and him!" She pointed a trembling finger at the camp commandant, at the chief of the state security and the commander of the guard. "Into the crazy house with them! Right away! Now!"

The duty officer tried to seize her and take her away, but she resisted him vigorously, and began to scream and curse. He finally succeeded in getting a firm grip on her, and with a deft, hardly noticeable movement, twisted her arm behind her back. At the entrance of the dispensary

[3] Parrots with candles. Prisoner slang for guards with rifles, suggested by the manner in which they perform their duties from positions in the watchtowers.

appeared a woman in a white smock, evidently a doctor. The camp commandant shouted at her to call for aid personnel.

The crazy woman broke away from the duty officer once more, and ran up to me again. "You tell Comrade Stalin that I'm waiting for him to come and see me here. Tell him to come. I sent him a letter explaining all details. . . . Did he get my letter? Did he get it? Tell me, did he get it?"

I didn't know what to say. I told her that Comrade Stalin had received all her letters, and that everything would be all right. She immediately took on an important air. "In that case, I'll start off to Moscow tomorrow. Tell him that–tomorrow I leave." She continued to talk in a lower voice, half to herself.

From the dispensary five strongly-built female prisoner-aid women ran up to us with bedsheets in their hands. They stood indecisively before the crazy woman, until the commandant gave them a sharp order. Thereupon they fell upon the woman and bound her hand and foot with the twisted sheets, picked her up and carried her off toward the dispensary. She contorted her body, and continued to scream hysterically. "Him! Take him, that crazy commandant! Arrest that new one there, too, the one who just arrived! He's lying! He's a fake! He's lying; Comrade Stalin didn't send him! He's lying! lying! lying!"

They took her inside the dispensary. From inside her howling was still plainly audible. We continued on our way.

"Who is she, anyway?" I asked the camp commandant.

"Nobody important–it's all nonsense." Not wishing to answer me, he made a sweeping gesture with his hand to dismiss the matter.

"Crazy," the chief of the state security section said, and turning to the commandant, asked, "Why haven't they sent her away yet? That will have to be attended to as soon as possible. . . ."

I asked no further questions about the woman.

We passed by one barrack, alongside of which stood a group of about ten women. I was struck by the exceptional beauty of one of them. She appeared to be between twenty-three and twenty-five years old. Her figure, as well as her posture, suggested a certain conscious, vulgar coquettishness. Leaning with her shoulder against the wall, with one hand on her hip, she looked impudently at us, with a certain provocative, derisive look on her face. We stopped in front of the group. The camp commandant began to question them as to what brigade they were, and why they were not at work. It turned out that all of them had been excused from work because of illness.

The pretty one, without moving or changing her pose, said to the commandant, "Citizen Commandant, may I ask a question of the visiting officer?"

"You and your tired old jokes again! Now get this. If you insist on keeping on like this, you'll be in for plenty of trouble."

"Citizen Chief!" She addressed herself now directly to me, "Why don't you ask me why I'm here?"

"Well, if you want to, tell me then," I answered.

"I'm the wife of an enemy of the people—my husband was an important Chekist, and a member of the Central Committee of the Party," she blurted out quickly, as if she had memorized it. She burst into a loud, nervous, unnatural laughter at her "joke," and ran into the barrack.

The other prisoners registered disapproval of the conduct

of their young friend: "She's stupid. Still young. She'll cool off after a while. She's lying on her cot right now, crying. That's always the way with her."

"What we're going to do with her—I just don't know," the camp commandant said, after we had walked on a bit farther. "How many times have I had her up before me—warned her. It doesn't do any good. She apologizes, asks for forgiveness, and then goes right back and causes another incident."

"She's a spiteful bitch. She does it on purpose, just to cause trouble," said the chief of the state security section.

I wanted very much to find out more about her, but I suppressed my impertinent curiosity.

We came up to a structure which was standing apart from the barracks buildings. "Now here is our artists' 'atelier'," said the camp commandant, with ironic emphasis on the final word. We entered the building.

In the first room we entered, sitting at small tables, arranged near the windows, several women with various types of engraving tools were engaged in carving wood and bone. Some of them were working through magnifying glasses. One of the prisoners, a brigadier, smiling courteously, began to explain the work which her brigade was doing, and to show us the finished products.

There was a fantastically varied assortment. There were artistically contrived cigar-cases, covers for the binding of albums, bas-reliefs, monograms, mosaic work and bone carvings, picture frames, baguettes, desk sets, paperknives, caskets, fine engraving and others of a similar type.

We lost ourselves in admiration of this exquisite handicraft. Several of the articles were so delicately and intricately executed that it was possible to examine them satisfactorily only through a magnifying glass. The artistic themes were widely varied; for example, propaganda on Soviet themes, with allegorical depictions of industry and agriculture in the five-year plans, the power and force of the Red Army, the coming victory of communism in the entire world, the greatness of Stalin, and so forth. Some of them were fantasy, or illustrations of Russian folk tales and legends.

We examined a matchcase, still uncompleted. It was an astounding piece of workmanship—a carved mosaic. On the tiny pieces was carving with delicate illustrations. On this work one prisoner had already been working six months, and according to her own estimates, she would require an equal length of time to complete it. I looked at the intricate drawings through a large magnifying glass, and the meticulousness of the work astounded me, as did its utter uselessness. It was intended as a gift for People's Commissar for Internal Affairs Beria, but it seemed to me that it belonged instead in a museum of fine art.

We proceeded to the next room, where embroideresses were at work. Here silk panels were stretched on frames. The prisoners were working on them with great care. Here they were making Gobelins, lampshades, carpets, capes, ladies' handkerchiefs, and other things. We watched them at work, and admired their products. Everything being made here was intended to become gifts for exalted figures of the NKVD in Moscow, or was being produced at their order. The cost was minimal, naturally.

In the next room which we entered the prisoners were painting pictures. They painted, not from nature, of course, but from lithograph reproductions of the work of famous artists, procured from the Tret'yakovsky Art Gallery in

Moscow. They were painting on little caskets, on glassware, on small knick-knacks, on toilet and smoking articles, and the like. They were also painting on silk cloth to be used for dresses, kerchiefs and drapes.

In my fascination with all this wealth of artwork, I was paying no attention whatever to anyone else in the room. Suddenly I heard a loud exclamation, and a feminine voice, strangely familiar to me. "Good Lord! Can it really be you? Here?"

I turned quickly. Two paces away, looking at me with astonishment, a woman was standing with brushes and a palette in her hands. Like a kaleidoscope, the reminiscences flashed through my head . . . 1933. Moscow, Leningradskoe Chaussee, Shakovaya Ulitsa 10, Maria Georgievna Petrova. My neighbor in the next apartment. An artist. . . . What an artist! Her whole room used to be covered with pictures she had painted. The doors, the walls, the ceiling, the window frames, the curtains, even the furniture, everything was embellished with intricate patterns and drawings. Her husband, Gleb Vasil'evich Petrov, an officer of the Air Forces, small, heavy-set, always jolly, never despondent, always convivial—a wonderful fellow. He was fond of good company and good drink. . . . Their son Jura—he was five years old then—was a thin, weak, nervous urchin. He was too small for his years. A naughty boy he was, always causing embarrassment to his parents. He had a husky voice, just like Maria Georgievna, and resembled her in face and manner as well.

Maria Georgievna was by no means a beautiful woman. On the contrary, she was rather homely, short of stature, and thin. She had a narrow face, on which the most prominent feature was her large nose. Nevertheless, there was something inexplicably fascinating about her. She was a happy, cultured and well-educated woman. She and her husband enjoyed company, and their house had always been open to their wide circle of friends. She was good at listening, told stories well, and had an exceptional talent for dispersing a bad mood and putting everyone in a good humor. She was the life of the party, as the saying goes, and it was simply impossible to be depressed in her presence. In short, she was a remarkable woman.

How old could she have been in those days? Difficult to say. From her appearance she could have been from twenty-six to twenty-eight, perhaps a bit older. The position of the Petrov family had been greatly enhanced by the fact that Maria Georgievna was a friend from school days of the wife of Deputy People's Commissar for Defense Marshal Tukachevsky. She was a frequent guest in the home of her girlhood friend, and knew many of the high-ranking persons who used to come there.

For more than six years we had been neighbors in the same house, and the very best of relationships had prevailed between us. She moved away in 1933, and I didn't see her again. In later years some very vague rumors reached me to the effect that Maria Georgievna had separated from her husband and married for a second time. I never heard any more about the family.

All this flashed through my mind in that instant of my encounter with her. Here she was, in a camp for family members of traitors to the homeland—a prisoner, and I. . . .

No need to describe the feelings which this unexpected meeting evoked in me; my impulses, the warmth, the emotion which I could hardly control. I took myself in hand and, trying to give my voice a completely non-committal tone: "Ah! You here? For the first husband, or the second?"

"Because of the Tukachevsky affair, along with Gleb Vasil'evich," she answered me in a quiet voice, and began to weep. "They locked up my second husband also, as an enemy of the people," she added, wiping the tears away with a handkerchief.

I glanced at the chief of the state security section standing near me. He was listening attentively to our conversation, with evident curiosity.

"You've met someone you know?" said the camp commandant with a smile, coming over to us.

I wasn't feeling well at all. What the devil had drawn me into these art shops, I thought to myself. If I had taken my departure this morning, as I had originally planned, all this would not have happened. Now on my return to my own headquarters I could expect all kinds of unpleasant explanations, perhaps even an interrogation.

In order to conceal my agitation and fear, I asked Maria Georgievna to show me the picture she was painting. I gave her a cigarette; that is, I offered all the prisoners cigarettes, in order not to single her out. Then, as if absent-mindedly, I left the newly-opened pack on the table. I knew very well how much pleasure it would bring them. It was all I could do.

I wanted only one thing—to get out of this place as soon as possible. I wanted to meet no more ChSIR's, no more former wives of fallen great men. I felt that I was done for. I didn't want to see any more fine art. I was thinking of another kind of art now—the art of getting out of this dangerous situation into which I had landed myself by my curiosity. I was quite certain that immediately after our departure Maria Georgievna would tell her prisoner friends about our former friendship. I was also certain that she would be called up this very day by the chief of the state security section, who would interrogate her for information about me and our relationship with one another. I would probably be accused of having had a connection with Marshal Tukachevsky, whom I knew only from portraits. . . .

We returned by the same route over which we had come. I didn't look at anything more; I paid no attention to what was being explained to me. I was preoccupied with what she could tell about me. I was trying to remember every trifling incident in our long acquaintance, and although I could think of nothing specifically derogatory, the uneasiness did not leave me.

My reflections were interrupted by a piercing scream. I looked in the direction from which it had come. I saw through the barred window of the camp dispensary a completely naked woman, standing on the windowsill. Holding onto the bars with one hand, she was energetically waving the other, and making weird movements with her body. As we came closer, it was possible to make some sense out of her threats and curses. Pointing at me, she screamed furiously, "The new one! The new one! Take him away! That one there in the red cap. He's a fraud! He's not from Stalin! He's only lying; don't believe him!"

Someone seized her from inside, and the window was slammed shut.

We were passing by the prisoners' barracks. Women were standing in front of several of the entrances. I avoided looking at them.

"Here's where the tailor shops are located," said the camp commandant, pointing out a long barrack to me. "If you'd like we'll stop in and have a look. There are three hundred prisoners here, all working together in one room."

This proposal terrified me; I declined the invitation. The camp commandant suggested that I might like to inspect the construction on the new buildings, where more than a thousand prisoners were at work. I declined this also. My apprehension over the meeting with Maria Georgievna would not leave me.

After dinner I called on the chief of the state security section, in order to forestall any possible question on his part. In a nonchalant tone I began to tell him about Maria Georgievna, about her husband and about my acquaintance with them.

"Of all the people to meet up with," I said, "who would have thought that her husband, an important officer of the air force, would turn out to be an enemy of the people? Comrade Stalin knows what he's talking about, when he warns us to be eternally vigilant and skeptical toward one's surrounding, even one's closest acquaintances. . . ."

The chief of the state security section, it seemed, was listening to me with indifference. But what was he thinking? As for me, I was thinking only of how I could head him off without betraying my internal concern, how I could show him that this meeting had not disturbed me, and that I did not intend to conceal anything connected with it. "Tell me," I said, "would it be possible for me to see this prisoner's dossier? I'll have to make a report of this meeting to my own chief when I return. He might ask me what she's in here for. It might be embarrassing if I didn't know the particulars of the charge. . . ."

"Yes, of course," he answered, "but you won't be able to find out a thing from her dossier."

I said that I would like to see it, just the same.

He picked up the telephone, and in a dry, authoritative voice, ordered, "Bring me immediately dossier number 138645—Maria Georgievna Petrova-Brenner."

"What the devil is this," I thought. "He's already made inquiries. He's got her full name and dossier number on the tip of his tongue. He'll call her up this very day for a special interrogation, and he'll write up a report of the whole incident. Maybe he's already called her in; maybe he's already made his report. . . ."

The dossier was brought. Bound in it was only a single half-sheet of paper. The text read as follows:

EXTRACT FROM THE MINUTES
OF THE SPECIAL CONFERENCE

CASE	DISPOSITION
Case of enemy of the people, Maria Georgievna Petrova-Brenner, born 1905.	Confine in camp with strict isolation for a period of ten years.

Secretary of Special Conference	Signature

"And this is the complete dossier?" I asked.

"Everything," the chief of the state security section answered me laconically, looking at me with a mocking smile, "What more could you want? Short and to the point."

"Then I'll make a note of the decision and the dossier number."

"No, I can't permit that; it's forbidden. Just write down the name and surname, that will be sufficient. You see—she's a personal acquaintance of yours."

These last words jarred me. I thanked him for the information which I had received, took my departure and, upon leaving the building, made for the main gate, where horses were waiting for me, to take me to the station.

* * *

Two small tousled Kazakh horses quickly sped the carriage over the smooth road through the steppe. The commander of the guard was riding along with me, escorting me to the station. We rode in silence. I was preoccupied with disturbing thoughts about the possible consequences of today's meeting with the chief of the state security section. This self-assured, boastful young Chekist had turned out to be very dangerous to me. I remembered the guarded interest with which he had listened to my conversation with Maria Georgievna, and his malicious allusion during our final conversation to my "acquaintance" with a ChSIR prisoner. There was no way out of it; I would absolutely have to report the details of this incident to my superiors.

I didn't want the commander of the guard to notice my state of mind. I started up a conversation with him. "An interesting assortment you have here," I said to him.

"Much too interesting," he answered. "So interesting that you can't prevent incidents with them. Not a day goes by that one of the soldiers or another isn't called in to the state security section for an interrogation. You simply can't imagine how much trouble and unpleasantness I have to go through because of this. Somebody says something or does something, and they accuse me. I don't instruct my subordinates properly, they say. I neglect my responsibilities for political instruction, and so forth. I don't know what

I'm going to do. I'm lucky that I happen to have an exceptionally good commissar. This makes it possible to get along at least to a certain extent.

"There are plenty of instances of misconduct on the part of the soldiers, of course. It's one unending struggle against infractions of one kind or another. But how can you cope with them? Reprimands are absolutely without effect. Deprive them of leave, you'll say. But no leave is granted in this camp in any case. Put them in arrest, you're thinking. But that's no punishment; the soldiers like it. It's a chance to catch up on their sleep. After all, ten to twelve hours on duty every day, and then after that two or three hours of exercises of various kinds, and meetings of one kind or another. Spending a few days in the guard house is a real break for them. The only thing which has any effect is to bring them to trial for every infraction, no matter how slight. But you have to use common sense here, too. If I have too many of them locked up, the unit's court martial record looks bad. I'd be accused myself, of corrupting the guard. I'd be the one who'd wind up before a court.

"Let me give you an example of what I'm up against. When the ChSIR's first began to come to the camp, a lot of them had many fine personal articles. They had been permitted to bring with them two large suitcases of personal effects; all of their other possessions had been confiscated by the state. They brought a lot of clothing, linens and the like. They hoped it would last them for several years, for the entire period of their confinement. Any expensive items which they had, such as watches, rings, bracelets, chains and the like, were taken away from them and impounded in the treasury, so they couldn't be used as bribes. We didn't consider that the rags, the clothing would be negotiable. We let them keep it all.

"What do you suppose happened? Our soldiers, our camp administrative personnel, began to barter for these things with the prisoners, in exchange for bread, for tobacco. They even brought vodka into the camp in order to trade it for rags of various kinds. They set up a regular bazaar in the barracks! An utterly impossible state of affairs. What kind of discipline can you have under such conditions? We took severe measures, of course. The soldiers were forbidden to enter the camp except when it was officially and actually necessary. Every week we made surprise searches in the *kaserne*, as well as in the family quarters of the married soldiers. The bartered articles would be confiscated, and the guilty parties would be punished. This brought a halt to the wholesale trade, but secretly they continue it. It's going on right now. It's impossible to isolate the soldiers from the prisoners, no matter what measures you take. They perform duties inside the camp, guard the work details, stand sentry duty, perform escort service. During this time they talk about all manner of things with the prisoners. So our attempt to stamp out the black marketing has really resulted only in causing another type of infraction: violation of orders. Do you know what a state of affairs things have come to be? The soldiers return from their posts, or from duty in the barracks area, and the chief of the state security section and I wait for them inside the *kaserne*, or else we meet them as they go through the gates. You take some soldier or other into a separate room and tell him to strip off his clothes. They're afraid, of course. They try to protest that they don't have any contraband.

And then you find it on them, underneath their uniforms: ladies' underwear, handkerchiefs, petticoats, sheets and so forth, wrapped around their bodies.

"Then the interrogations start, and the investigations. And what defenses they put up! 'My wife doesn't have anything to wear. I can't buy anything anywhere; where am I suppose to get it from?'

We punish them, and we publicize the punishments at meetings. It doesn't help a bit. You'd be surprised; when such things are brought up for discussion at meetings, the soldiers come out actively. They condemn the violators, condemn the infractions, they draw up beautiful resolutions, petition the command to take stern and decisive measures against the offenders, and so forth. As a matter of fact, the 'conscientious' ones, the ones who take the initiative in proposing the actions, are guilty of the very same thing themselves. These meetings are very dramatic sessions. These lads are wonderful actors, every one of them. It's a terrific show.

"And then, there's the problem of intimacies between the soldiers and the prisoners. Almost every soldier has his sweetheart among them. Don't think it's only among the bachelors, either; the married ones do it too. It's forbidden of course, and when discovered, is severely punished. But this doesn't stop the business. They make their arrangements beforehand, and meet either by day, during working hours on the *steppe*, or at night, when they're on sentry duty inside the camp. Besides, despite the order against visiting the camp outside of duty hours, they find valid pretexts of one kind or another. You see, the dispensary system, the warehouses, the shops, the offices and so forth, are all located within the confines of the camp. So under the pretext of visiting them the soldiers may rather easily get into the camp outside of duty hours and associate with the prisoners, whenever they take a notion to do so.

"It's very difficult to prevent intimacies. The soldiers are young, healthy boys, they have their physical needs. We are not allowed to give them passes, either to the city, which is twenty kilometers away, or even to the village here. There's nowhere for them to walk, nowhere they can amuse themselves. Their whole life is confined to the *kaserne*. You can imagine that all kinds of ideas get into their heads in such a situation. And as for the prisoners, especially the young ones, they're not without feeling, either. And furthermore, hunger and need also play a certain role. After all, their soldier sweethearts help them in various ways, give them things which they have exchanged with other prisoners; bread and other things to eat. They buy things for them in the store. So the relationship is based on mutual interests. This all greatly undermines discipline, and gives rise to all kinds of violations and abuses. These offenses often take very serious forms, and have dangerous consequences. The soldiers illegally send off letters for their prisoner-sweethearts and their friends. In the soldiers' names they write letters to their acquaintances and relatives. It's impossible to check up on it. You see, the soldiers don't send the letters through the military post, where all correspondence undergoes the strictest of censorship. Instead they find other means, for example, the duty trains, with the connivance of the convoy troops. Sooner or later we find out about it, but it's not always possible to prove it and formally prefer charges. True, we've convicted some of them, and sent them off to isolation camps.

"All this, of course, is a direct result of the soldiers intimacies with the prisoners. We often make searches of the soldiers' effects. Sometimes we do it in their presence, and sometimes when they are away. The searches are usually made as a surprise. And the things we find in their bags! Women's underwear, stockings, eau de cologne, powder and so forth, to say nothing of packages of food products all wrapped up ready to give to the prisoners–vodka too.

"You ask some unmarried soldier, 'Why do you keep women's underwear and powder in your bag?' And he'll answer, 'I was getting it ready to send home to my sister. . . .' Check up, and you find that he doesn't have a sister. One time we found a package with ladies' underwear in the bag of a soldier who was the secretary of our local party organization. This almost caused a terrific scandal. After all, he was the party secretary. It didn't make us happy to find this little treasure. It's a serious matter to find compromising material in the possession of a party secretary; and to allow it to go unpunished is still worse. Fortunately he didn't admit his guilt, and one soldier helped him out of the mess by declaring that the things belonged, not to the party secretary, but to him, and that he was preparing to send them home to the *kolkhoz.* We pretended that we believed him, and hushed the matter up. It was absolutely clear, of course, what the package was intended for, and to whom it belonged. The soldiers helped out the party secretary, and on another occasion this secretary diplomatically returned the favor. They're practically all guilty of some sin or other, and so they cover for one another, help each other out, try to smooth things over when somebody gets into trouble. 'One hand washes the other,' they say. You simply couldn't get along without it. So the only way we can track down these offenses is by the use of informants. Some *seksot*[4] informs on his comrades–of course, they behave just as outrageously themselves, but the state security looks on it with indulgence. Otherwise, of course, the informants wouldn't be able to win the confidence of the other soldiers, and they wouldn't be able to run down the violations. The *seksots* know this very well, and take full advantage of it."

We were riding past a work project on which several hundred prisoners were engaged in the preparation of *Karagannik* fuel. *Karagannik* is a *steppe* vegetation in the form of a low dwarfed thick bush, used in Kazakhstan for the heating of stoves. The great area in which the prisoners were working was ringed by guards stationed at intervals of a hundred to a hundred and fifty meters from each other. The commander said to me with a sly smile, "What do you say we stop here and act as if we're going to go over to the work area. You'll see the soldiers giving each other warning signals of our approach."

The carriage stopped. We got out and started to walk toward the work area. Somewhere in the distance a sharp whistle was heard, then farther off another, and still farther a third, hardly audible. Then, from various points in the distance, could be heard others.

"Do you hear it? Already they all know that danger is approaching. They pass the signals along down the line. You won't find any violations here. Any soldier who was sleeping, or any prisoner, is awake now, and is standing in

[4] *Seksot.* Abbreviation for "sekretnyi sotrudnik" ("secret collaborator.") Not used in official terminology. It is a derogatory term for a secret informer of the state security organs.

his place, or doing her work. Go ahead, check them. The signals were only given, of course, because we stopped. It's a remarkable system of mutual assistance."

We returned to the carriage and continued on our way. The commander went on with his story. We had known each other for several years, and he was frank with me.

"Now and then scandals occur among the soldiers themselves because of jealousy over the female prisoners. The very same kind of rows occur between wives and husbands. The wives learn of their husbands' intimacies with the prisoner women, scenes take place, and the wives contrive, by fantastic ruses and refined trickery, to get into the camp and cause uproars with their prisoner-rivals. It actually comes to blows. These affairs, unpleasant as they are, give great pleasure to the chief of the state security section. You see, that's his bread and butter."

I started to laugh, and the commander, perceiving my disbelief, continued, "You're laughing; you don't believe it, but it's the truth. In these affairs he always comes to the support of the outraged wives, calls them into his office, sympathizes with them, talks for long periods with them, condemning their faithless husbands. By making use of their anger and fanning their jealousy he turns these women into informants against their own husbands, and pries out their most closely guarded secrets. In a fit of jealousy these stupid females spill plenty. Later, of course, they regret it deeply, but it's too late by that time.

"Perhaps you may recall an incident which occurred here last year; we submitted a report on it. The murder, by a sentry, of one of the prisoners and a young officer of the guard."

I did indeed remember this incident, both from the initial

reports, and from the details of the investigation which followed. Officially the incident was described in the following manner: At night the soldier was standing on post on a guard tower near the barbed wire fence of the camp. A woman came out of the barrack, which was located not far from the tower, and disregarding the warnings of the sentry, started toward some buildings which were under construction near the wire. The sentry shot into the air, but the prisoner paid no attention to the warning. Thereupon he shot her. At the sound of the shot a junior officer, the officer on duty in the camp, ran to the scene of the incident, but the sentry, not recognizing him in the darkness, shot again, and killed him also. Such was the official version.

I told the commander that I was acquainted with the incident. He laughed and said to me, "The business is a matter of the past now, and I can tell you now how it really was." He related to me the following tragic story: "One of the soldiers was having an affair with a prisoner, a pretty young thing. The relationship had continued between them for several months. He was passionately in love with her; gave her all kinds of gifts. We knew about this, of course, just as we knew about many other cases, but there was no concrete evidence. The soldier had been called up several times for interrogation, but he stubbornly denied the liaison. The prisoner denied the affair also.

"The usual procedure in a case like this would be to transfer him to another unit, but we couldn't do this, since all transfers from this camp are forbidden. The soldiers know too much. We couldn't transfer the prisoner to another place either, since she was a ChSIR. Things went on like this for several months. One young officer, who was also very much taken by the prisoner, attempted to make advances to her. For a long time he courted her, but without result. She didn't accept his attentions.

"The situation caused a smouldering hatred between the two rivals, but they didn't betray each other. Everybody knew about this hatred however, as well as the reason for it. The officer, taking advantage of his official position, made things hard for the soldier. He had him assigned to the most difficult details, in places where he would not be able to meet with his sweetheart.

"After a few months the officer was finally successful in achieving his goal: the girl became intimate with him. The friction between the officer and the soldier developed to such intensity that in order to avoid an incident the soldier was transferred to another platoon.

"By means of a certain amount of manipulation the soldier got himself appointed to the detail guarding the camp periphery. By agreement with a friend, who was also assigned to this detail, he took his assigned place—as guard on a tower located only a few meters from the barrack in which his former sweetheart was quartered. The platoon leader permitted the change, since he could see nothing wrong in it.

"As it happened, on that very night the young officer, the soldier's rival, was detailed as camp duty officer. Evidently the jealous soldier had waited for a long time for the situation which now developed—made to order for his purposes, you might say.

"That night the soldier, standing duty on the tower, saw the duty officer go into the barrack. A few minutes later he came out and turned in the direction of the bachelor officers' quarters, located not far away. After a little while the soldier saw his sweetheart come out and also go off in the same direction. Later on, when she returned to her barrack, he shot her without any warning and killed her on the spot. After the first shot he fired a few more times into the air.

"The duty officer, hearing the shots and not understanding immediately what the situation was, ran to the scene of the shooting. The soldier killed him also, and continued to fire into the air and sound the alarm. At all posts the searchlights were turned on, and colored rockets were sent up. The camp was surrounded, and an alert group with a machine gun was assigned to the post from which the shooting had occurred. The two bodies lay there, quite close to each other.

"There was a big scandal. Everybody knew very well what had happened. The soldier was immediately arrested, and an investigation was ordered. During interrogation he firmly stuck to his story. He maintained that, on seeing a prisoner unknown to him coming out of the barrack, making for the wire, he warned her twice with shouts, and with a shot in the air. Then he was obliged to shoot her, because she did not obey his order, and was trying to conceal herself from his field of vision. Right after this he saw another figure, hiding behind buildings, perceivable only with difficulty in the darkness. Once again he gave warnings, but since he got no answer, he was obliged to fire again, hitting the duty officer, as it became clear to him only subsequently.

"Formally, the actions of the soldier were recognized as correct, quite in accordance with standing instructions. But everybody knew exactly what had happened and why. Since nothing could be proven, the official position was taken that the incident had transpired just as the soldier had maintained. The court acquitted him. It was to nobody's advantage to establish the truth.

"Do you see now, what it's like here?" The commander asked, as he finished his story. He went on again: "You are certainly aware that during the past two years, in my unit alone, which consists of five hundred men, eighteen soldiers and one officer have been sentenced; and I anticipate that during the next few days several more will be brought before trial for anti-Soviet agitation. And what kind of anti-Soviet agitation is it? Repeating the fantasies these females concoct, that's all. But in all these fabrications there must be some truth, otherwise they wouldn't have been so severely punished for repeating them. But tell me, is this counter-revolution?

"Now take me, for example. I'm an officer. I'm a Communist. I see and hear a lot here. If I keep silent about it—everything's all right. But if I talk about something I know, immediately I become a counterrevolutionary. How can that be?"

He fell silent then, and gave himself over to his private thoughts for awhile.

"Comrade Chief!" he suddenly said to me after some period of silence, "I wanted to ask you about a matter which is very important to me—a favor. Please get me transferred to some other organization. I know that transfers are forbidden for us, but surely there could be one exception. . . . On my word of honor, I can't stay here any longer. I can't stand it anymore. I'm afraid I'll wind up before a court for something or other. . . . Transfer me please, I beg you. . . ."

I told him that this was impossible.

"Then I'll go before a medical commission and get myself released from service for disability!"

"Are you really sick?" I asked.

"I could make it look as if I were sick."

"Then you'd wind up in a court for malingering, instead of for counterrevolution," I answered him, clapping him on the shoulder in a friendly way, in order to show my sympathy, and understanding for his situation.

"Better to go before a court for malingering than for counterrevolution," he retorted in irritation, and we again fell silent. To the very end of our inspection tour we did not say another single word to each other.

As we rode up to the station we saw in the distance, a little to one side, a great deal of activity in the assembly area. The area was closely surrounded by soldiers of the convoy troops of the NKVD. They were easy to recognize by their bright uniforms. On the railroad siding, five special prisoner cars were standing. One by one female prisoners were being led out of the cars, and each one was being carefully checked off on the manifest, and turned over to the receptionist from the camp. A few paces from the cars, standing in formation in ranks of four, were the prisoners who had already been received, surrounded by the soldiers of the camp guard. Nearby stood several wagons, piled high with the prisoners' possessions–suitcases, bundles, bags. On top of the baggage were sitting some old and sick women, too weak to stand in the formation. Forming a general perimeter around the whole scene at a distance of a hundred and fifty meters were pacing soldiers with rifles, driving off curious persons, preventing their approach, keeping them moving.

A short distance away was standing a group of soldiers from the convoy troops, about twenty men, equipped with two machine guns, led by an officer—the reserve, ready for action in the event of any extraordinary incidents.

It was a new shipment of Family Members of Traitors to the Homeland, consigned to the special Akmolinsk camp for ChSIR's.

We came up to the station. My train was already standing at the platform, and there remained only a few minutes until its departure. Going onto the platform, we stopped by the side of my car, each of us thinking his private thoughts.

The signal for the departure of the train was given. We said good-by, firmly pressing each other's hand. I got on the train. Looking out of the window, I saw that the commander was standing on the platform by the side of my car. The train started to move.

The commander, waving his hand to me, shouted, as the train pulled away, "Have a good trip, Comrade Chief! Please don't forget about my request. . . . You're my only hope!"

JUL'FA

I

THE police training school for dogs is located on a great open plain, not far from the central administration area of the concentration camp in northern Kazakhstan. Here dogs are trained for operational duties with the internal troops and with the organs of state security. Instructors and handlers are trained in the same school.

As we came in sight of the school it was possible to make out low buildings with flat roofs, and when we approached closer we could hear distinctly the sharp, penetrating barking of the dogs. We had no sooner entered the breeding kennels when an entire litter of puppies descended upon us. Tousled little things they were, with silky fur and delicate, slender little tails pointing up into the air. They rollicked about, clambered over each other, stumbled, pushed one another with their legs. They stretched out their little noses to us, looking for caresses, and treats. Their mother, a thoroughbred German shepherd no longer young, with a sagging abdomen, stood off at a distance, quietly, not moving, and kept an eye on the behavior of her little ones.

Out from behind the corner of a building sprang still another litter, and yet another and another, barking shrilly, squeakily. We were surrounded by dozens on dozens of puppies, crowding around us merrily, playing, wriggling, fawning. We could hardly extricate ourselves from this playful invasion; they simply would not leave us alone. They romped among themselves, chasing one another, growling ridiculously, biting. The littlest ones begged to be picked up. They snuggled in our arms, three to five together, burying their noses, and lay quietly until they were put down on the ground again.

The mothers also wanted to come to us, but the soldier-handlers gently restrained them, and kept them at a distance. Full-grown service dogs cannot be permitted to associate with outsiders, lest they develop the trait of sociability, which is harmful for them, and spoils their operational qualities.

The dogs are put through a ten-month course of instruction to train them for service-search duties. It takes place at various times of the year, and trains them to operate under all kinds of conditions and in every kind of weather. It is a complicated and strenuous training. From the very beginning, a dog is assigned exclusively to one person, who will train her, and after completion of her education, will work with her. The handlers are trained right along with the dogs. The course is founded upon what is called "the disciplinary cycle." It begins with the teaching of movement methods, halting, sitting, mounting vehicles, the execution of simple commands, rejection of food and caresses from strangers, other dogs, animals, or any other outside influence.

The intermediate phase of training involves more complicated assignments: high jumping and broad jumping, overcoming obstacles, movement over narrow planks and logs, jumping into windows and narrow apertures, jumping along with their handlers, and onto moving objects. The dogs are inured to noises, even gunfire.

A later training phase emphasizes pursuit, and restraint of persons upon command and signals. The dogs are taught the principles of defense, and of attack on armed and unarmed persons, combat techniques–how to seize an opponent–and so forth. They are taught to guard objects, buildings, persons. When ordered, a dog will sit for hours and guard an object, not moving from her place. Except for her handler, she allows no one to approach it, even should he be known to her. Upon the approach of a stranger she growls a warning. If this is not heeded she calls for help by barking. If any person attempts to take the guarded object, to enter a guarded building, or if a person under guard attempts to escape, the dog attacks him, using her teeth. When on guard she allows no one to approach her. She will attack an intruder, but will not leave the object which she is guarding. In such a situation she barks continuously to give alarm concerning the intruder on her post.

The final period of training is the most difficult and protracted of all. During this stage the dogs are developed in the techniques of picking up scents, tracking, and search of terrain. To be acceptable for service, they must be able to pick up a trail in any kind of weather. Under favorable conditions some exceptionally well-trained dogs are capable of finding and taking up a scent even after it is eight hours old. Such dogs are quite rare, however. The overall standard for average dogs, considering all kinds of weather, soil trafficability and other factors, is that they be able to pick up a trail one and a half to two hours old. When the trail is fresh, they must be able to pick it up not only on dry land, but even in a marsh. If it is no more than fifteen to twenty minutes old a dog should be able to sense it even on the surface of water—on a lake or a river for example, since the molecules remain in the air above the water for a certain length of time.

The chief of the training school took me out with him onto the *steppe*, where the dogs were undergoing field training. We came upon a group of student-handlers who were standing in formation with their young dogs. One by one they were being called out to lead them on a loose rein about an area which had been strewn with pieces of meat. The tantalizing smell attracted the dogs' attention. When they saw the meat they would whine pleadingly, and look up at their masters as if to say, "May I take it?" The handlers feigned disinterest, and ignored the entreaties. Here a young dog could endure the temptation no longer, and furtively seized a piece of meat as she was being led past. With a piercing screech she immediately ejected it from her mouth, and pressed against her master, tail between her legs, gazing apprehensively at the trap. The meat was connected to a weak electric charge. The handler gave her a cut with his whip as punishment for her breach of discipline. Service dogs are strictly forbidden to pick up food lying on the ground. They may eat only from their bowls, or from the hands of their masters.

Further on we watched a group of dogs in whom the trait of savagery was being developed. One dog, held on a leash by her handler, was being harassed by trainers in special costumes blowing whistles at her and badgering her with clubs. The dog was trying to leap upon her tormenter, but she was being restrained by the leash. Only when her exasperation reached its very pinnacle was she released, whereupon with savage frenzy she leapt upon the trainer. Then her handler restrained her again, dragging her back forcefully, and quieted her with praise and caresses.

The special costume which the trainers wear is made of canvas and thick felt. A hood covers the head of the wearer, including the entire face, and the neck and throat. It has long sleeves which extend below the hands.

In a third group a trainer, dressed in the same kind of protective costume, was running about on the *steppe.* He was scrambling over specially erected fences, running over a narrow log across a broad pit, clambering up a ladder over a high wall, crawling through a small aperture, jumping down to the ground, and running farther and farther away over the *steppe.*

The dog was restrained on a leash until the proper moment. Then a command was given, and she was turned loose. Off she went at full speed after the fugitive. Without hesitating she cleared the fence in a single leap, flew over the ditch, followed the scent to the ladder, climbed up it, crawled through the hole, jumped down, and took off after her quarry. She overtook him and leapt on him from behind, snapping and tearing at him, trying to seize him by the hand or the throat. The trainer offered resistance, beating her with a club. She seized the club with her jaws, and without releasing her grip, quite gradually worked her jaws closer to the hand of her opponent. Seizing the hand, she worked her teeth farther up along the arm, trying to reach his throat. A battle ensued. In frenzy the dog tore at her victim, now fallen to the ground. The more opposition he offered, the more furious was her onslaught. The very slightest attempt at resistance—even a slight movement of the hand or leg, evoked fury in the dog. Now a handler ran up. He led the dog away, soothing her, caressing her.

The dogs bite with mortal grips. When they seize an opponent in their teeth they bite convulsively into him, with abnormal force. Even the dog herself is sometimes unable to relax this deathly grip. There are also "progressive grips," wherein the dog, having seized her opponent by the hand, releases him for an instant, grips again and again, ever higher and higher, working up toward the throat.

These young dogs in the *steppe* had already been undergoing training for two or three months, and in another month or two they would be ready to embark on a more complicated phase of instruction—discovery of a track, movement by scent, the search of terrain, locating a given object, and other related specialties.

The training course is scheduled for ten months. In practice it does not last that long however, since the dogs are always required at rates faster than they can be trained. From six to eight months is the normal length of the course. As it draws toward its close another young group of dogs has grown up and is ready for training. Thus it is from year to year. . . .

For search duty German shepherds are preferred. They are less capricious than other breeds, hardy, strong and versatile, and they adapt well to various climatic conditions. For sentry and escort duty, on the other hand, shepherd dogs from the Caucasus are used. These are enormous, shaggy, strong, vicious dogs. German shepherds from the search service are also used for sentry duty when they have received some kind of physical injury, or after they have grown too old for more active service. Sentry dogs can be trained more quickly and easily than search dogs; their course of instruction lasts only one or two months. However they, like the search dogs, must be able to engage in pursuit operations, to attack, to defend themselves, and to conduct terrain searches.

After watching the dogs train for a while, we went on to see their living quarters. These were located in a long low narrow building, a kind of closed-in corridor, divided into compartments. One side of this corridor-like structure was a wall in which were many small doors. On the other side there was no wall, but simply a screen of wire mesh. Beyond the screen were small open accommodations which provided a terrace for each dog. From these terraces doors led back into rooms of exactly the same size and shape as the terraces, but walled in. Thus each dog was provided a little apartment of her own. Each cabin was separated from the next by a wooden wall. The dogs lived in complete isolation in these accommodations, except when they were walked or exercised together. Over the door of each cabin was a little sign bearing the nickname and the age of the occupant. The dogs are fed in their cabins, exclusively by the persons who constantly attend them. No one is permitted contact with them except their handlers.

The interior of the cabins was clean and roomy. The paths leading through the area were strewn with fresh yellow sand. Everything was kept in meticulous order.

As I was passing by one of the screened-off cabins a little sign lettered in distinctive style attracted my attention. It bore a curious legend:

Honor Dog Jul'fa
Age 14 Years

I was surprised—fourteen years is generally considered the maximum normal life span of a dog. For service dogs it is most unusual to reach such an advanced age. The word "honor" on the little sign piqued my curiosity as to what interesting story there might be concerning this dog. I asked the chief of the kennels about it.

"What!" he said. "You've never heard of Jul'fa? Why she's famous. As a matter of fact, even her grandchildren and great-grandchildren are highly esteemed. Her reputation extends even to the central kennels in Moscow. Dogs with our Jul'fa's name in their pedigree are placed in a special category for that reason alone, and are valued above others, even though their actual performance may not be outstanding. Our Jul'fa hasn't been out of her cabin for five years. She's a tired old girl now. She can hardly move about. I can tell you some very interesting things about her, if you like."

I peered into the cabin through the metal screen. The forward half was empty. The chief of the kennels called Jul'fa loudly, several times, coaxing her in tender tones. She did not appear, and we had just about decided to go around the building and enter from the enclosed side. But just then, through the little door, the head of a dog appeared. She remained motionless for a few moments, her expressionless eyes turned in our direction. Then she slowly came out of her cabin, swaying on her feet and limping badly, dragging one hind leg along the ground. She came up to the screen where we were standing, and feebly lay down, closing her eyes.

"She's blind now," said the chief of the kennel. "She hasn't seen a thing for the last six months. She's losing her hearing; she hasn't a tooth in her head. Her left hind leg was broken in her last heroic fight five years ago. But if only you could have known her in the old days!" His voice expressed enthusiasm mingled with regret.

Jul'fa made a truly wretched appearance, despite the exclusive and tender care with which she was treated. She was thin and deformed; her hair was coming out in patches, denuding the whitish-pink skin underneath. Her legs were crooked. She trembled all over, even though the day was warm, and the sun was shining full upon her. She was fed by hand, with specially prepared food. The soldier-handlers considered it a privilege to care for Jul'fa. Not everybody was permitted the honor.

The chief of the kennels took a photograph out of his wallet and handed it to me. It showed the profile of a magnificent German shepherd. She had a sharp snout, and beautiful, erect ears. A smooth, sleek creature she was, with strong legs and a fluffy tail hanging downward in an arc, like a sabre.

"This was Jul'fa seven years ago, when I first met her," he said to me with pride. He stood there close by my side, admiring the photograph along with me.

It was difficult to imagine that such a beauty was this unfortunate, disfigured, toothless blind dog lying helplessly before us with torn-out fur, quivering, hardly able to move.

The chief went in to Jul'fa through a little wicket in the screen, and began to pet her. Without opening her eyes, she slowly, with difficulty raised her head a little, and licked his hand. She made no attempt to move, but lay there, breathing slowly and heavily.

II

Jul'fa's parents had been imported from Germany as part of a consignment of dogs for the introduction and development of service dog breeding in the USSR. Jul'fa herself had been born in the central kennels in Moscow. She began her service career with border guard duties, and soon distinguished herself among the border troops and among violators of the border as well, by her keen scent, her bravery, her intelligence, and her savagery in action. When Jul'fa was on border patrol the troops in her sector were confident that no trail left by a border crosser would escape her notice. They knew she would pick up the trail, and lead them to the exact place where the fugitives were hiding, however artfully they might have covered their tracks. Violators did not attempt crossings on the nights when Jul'fa was on duty. In the border troops it was said that would-be border crossers from either direction would make careful inquiries and reconnaissances before trying to cross. "Where is Jul'fa? Is she on duty tonight?"

Jul'fa was the pride of the border guards, and the mortal dread of border violators. Her first great feat on the border, the one which marked the beginning of her undying fame, came to pass in the following manner: One morning at dawn some border guards, patrolling the border with a search dog, came upon some human footprints, crossing into Soviet territory. The dog took up the scent and followed it through the woods. A few hundred paces farther on, the border guards discovered, hidden in the undergrowth, the corpse of one of their comrades. He had begun his tour of duty about an hour previously, so it was evident that the attack must have been very recent. An alarm was sent to *pogranzastav** and the guards meanwhile continued to follow the trail of the border crossers. They continued on through the woods and soon came to an open field by a

Pogranichnyi Zastav—Border Troop (Headquarters).

river whose near bank was high and steep. As the border-men approached the river they were greeted with gunfire from the other side. The dog and three guards were killed. The others, one of them wounded, lay down and began to return the fire. The shooting did not last long. One border crosser was killed. Two others concealed themselves on the opposite sloping bank of the river, which was covered with undergrowth.

A border alert group with dogs had been attracted by the shots, and now arrived at top speed. They forded the river and began to search for a trail which would indicate where the violators had hidden themselves. For more than an hour the border guards searched the bank of the river with dogs, but they were unable to determine the place where the fugitives had entered the water and where they had emerged. It was decided to call Jul'fa. Considerable time elapsed, however, before she could be gotten to the scene and could begin to look for the trail. After some searching she finally located it a few hundred meters downstream, and began to follow it. The border troops came after her. Jul'fa led the way into a village. She passed by several buildings, and then suddenly lunged toward one of the houses.

The owner came out. He answered all questions with professions of complete ignorance. Jul'fa however, would not be quieted. She kept straining at her leash toward the door of the house. The guards began a search. Jul'fa wanted to go down through a trapdoor in the floor, into the cellar.

When the trapdoor was opened shots were fired from below. Jul'fa's handler was killed. Jul'fa leaped into the opening, and disappeared into the darkness. A furious battle between the dog and the armed men ensued. None of the guards dared to look into the open hole for fear of being killed. All were afraid to shoot, for fear of killing Jul'fa. From the cellar, Jul'fa's furious snarling could be heard, mingled with the shouts and groans of the men. Another dog was let down into the cellar. There was a commotion—cries, groans, screams, shrieks. It went on like this for about ten minutes. And then, everything was silent. Jul'fa jumped up out of the cellar covered with blood, but unharmed. She ran up to her dead master, lying on the floor, and began to lick his face, howling dolefully.

When the guards went down into the cellar they found two border violators, terribly mangled, almost unconscious. The other dog, who had been wounded, lay near them in a pool of blood, licking herself.

The border crossers were taken away.

Jul'fa would not leave her dead master, even for a moment. At his funeral ceremony she whimpered lowly, pitifully. . . .

She was assigned to another handler. He tried diligently for a month, but was unable to get any response from her. At length it was decided that she would have to be transferred to the kennels for a time. After a period there she was sent back to duty, but on another sector of the border. Very gradually, very slowly she recovered, and at last regained her prior standards of distinguished border service. . . .

One time, in the middle of winter, during a heavy snowstorm, two bordermen failed to return on schedule from patrol. When they became several hours overdue, uneasiness developed in the headquarters. Although the storm was raging fiercely, a search party was dispatched to look for the missing men. Jul'fa went with them.

Several hours later the two bordermen who had lost their way returned to headquarters, but the group with Jul'fa who had been sent out to search for them did not return. Night set in.

This portion of the border in the Far East is located in sparsely settled, wild *taiga*. It is very easy to become lost in weather such as this, even when you know the area very well. The storm was still raging at dawn the next day. Two additional search groups with dogs were sent out.

Then, a little later, Jul'fa turned up at the headquarters. She was white, covered with powdered snow, and exhausted. Her stomach was drawn in, and her ribs protruded sharply. With a bark she burst into the door, and rushed about excitedly, barking, howling. The bordermen clustered about and examined her, to see whether she were wounded. She was unharmed, but would not be quieted. A piece of cloth, tied into a knot, was fastened to her collar. They opened it up, and found a note written by her handler. The writing wavered, and was difficult to decipher. "We have lost our way," it read. "We are exhausted. We can't go on. We are freezing. Save us. Feed Jul'fa."

They gave Jul'fa food. She fell upon it greedily, gulping it, forgetting in that moment the discipline to which she had been trained.

An expedition was quickly organized—men on skis with stretchers and first-aid equipment. Minutes later Jul'fa was leading the bordermen through the hills, deep into the *taiga*. The wind was piercing, and the falling snow was so thick that it was impossible to see even two paces ahead. Jul'fa led onward at high speed. The men could hardly keep up with her, even on skis. They had to slow her down by means of a long leash.

It was two or three hours before the bordermen, led by Jul'fa, reached their freezing comrades. They were in a serious condition, with frostbitten faces, hands and legs. All would certainly have soon frozen to death, had they not been rescued. They were brought back to headquarters, and then sent off to the hospital. They recovered eventually, after a protracted convalescence, but did not return to the border unit, for they had become invalids. Jul'fa had lost her second master.

As a result of this experience Jul'fa herself became seriously ill, and was sent off to the hospital. Upon her recovery, special orders from Moscow directed her transfer to the central kennels, since her health had been seriously undermined, and she was no longer able to endure the severe climatic conditions attending border duty in the far east. Within half a year after her assignment to the central kennels, however, she was being used on operational duty in the search service of the Moscow criminal police. The new handler assigned to her was the man who was currently chief of the Kazakhstan kennels, and who was now telling me her story.

In the criminal search service Jul'fa distinguished herself as before, strengthening her already outstanding reputation. She skillfully discovered thefts, and participated in the rounding up of criminals. She had numerous encounters with armed robbers, in which she always emerged the victor. Several scars from knife and gunshot wounds, and broken bones which had knitted themselves testified eloquently to her operational-combat capabilities. Her handler shared in her successes and her honors.

During her Moscow days Jul'fa and her handler once received a call to the Kremlin for an assignment which lasted several days. For what purpose they were summoned, and what they did there in the Kremlin remained a closely guarded secret. The only information released was that the mission had been successfully accomplished. Jul'fa's handler was awarded an engraved watch bearing the inscription: "For distinguished accomplishment of a mission for the state."

Jul'fa's impaired health became worse however, and the quality of her work fell off. Her handler received a promotion, and he and Jul'fa were transferred to the service dog kennels located in the Kazakhstan concentration camp. Despite her undermined health Jul'fa impressed everyone by her outstanding performance of her new duties.

III

In the Soviet concentration camps great reliance is placed on service dogs. Without them it would be a hopeless task to guard the prisoners effectively. However, the supply of dogs is never adequate. Their life span is short, and their period of useful service even shorter. In the camps the demand for their services increases at a rate disproportionate to the time required for their breeding, rearing, and training.

When Jul'fa was in the camp in Kazakhstan there were over one hundred thousand prisoners, distributed over the great expanse of one hundred and fifty square kilometers. She very quickly distinguished herself. Within a short time she had become widely known not only among the guards and the camp administration, but among the prisoners as well. She had only to make an appearance in order to quell immediately any disorder among the prisoners. Even the most confirmed incorrigibles became meek when she appeared. All knew her, not only by reputation, but by sight as well. Sometimes, when it was necessary to suppress a disturbance among the prisoners, false rumors were circulated that she was in the area. These rumors had a frightening effect, even though it was manifestly impossible for Jul'fa to be present in all places where her presence was needed. Along with the fear which she inspired in the prisoners however, there was also a feeling of great esteem for her, and even a certain affection.

"There's a dog that *is* a dog," they would say. "There never was a dog like that one, and there never will be. They ought to give her the Order of Lenin." Some use to call her jokingly "Laureate of the Stalin Prize." Conversations like the following were typical:

"Did you hear, they've brought Jul'fa to us. We'll have to watch our step now."

"Ah, that isn't Jul'fa. I know Jul'fa well. What do you mean, that's Jul'fa?"

"All right, so maybe it isn't Jul'fa. Go up to the wire, why don't you? She'll show you whether she's Jul'fa or not."

Once there was a mutiny in one of the penal groups. Two hundred and fifty prisoners were involved. Incorrigibles, confirmed criminals they were, all of them living in the same one-floor detached barrack under reinforced guard. They refused to submit to discipline, and would not go out to work, despite all orders, warnings and threats. They had barricaded the entrance and windows of their barrack, and would not allow either the guards or members of the camp administration to enter. When the guards started to break down the doors to get into the barrack, the prisoners defended themselves with stones and clubs. The barrack was surrounded by armed soldiers. They shot into the air, threatened reprisals on the rebellious prisoners, all without any effect whatsoever.

It was wintertime, and the temperature was far below freezing. The prisoners were warned that if they continued to resist they would be driven out into the freezing weather. Thereupon the guards beat in all the window panes. The prisoners still refused to surrender. They plugged up the broken windows as best they could. When the cold penetrated into the barrack they began to dismantle the interior, and to burn the wooden parts in the stove. This could not protect them for long against the cold, of course—the fuel supply was quite limited. Besides, they had no food reserves. It was a senseless revolt, and could result only in needless victims, and retaliations. It was a spontaneous, unpremeditated affair, a reflection of the despair of men doomed to perish, rebelling against the terrible conditions of the camp.

The high command arrived at the scene of the incident. With them was a special detachment of guards with several service dogs. Jul'fa was among them. She sprang lightly to the ground from the light truck in which she was riding, and shook herself. In a leisurely, beautiful gait she walked beside her handler. Her ears were erect; she looked about with interest at the scene—as if assessing what kind of assignment was facing her here.

Inside the barrack agitated, frightened voices were heard: "Dogs! Dogs!" One of the prisoners shouted, "Who's afraid, the Stalinist scum!"

"Jul'fa! They've brought Jul'fa!"

The appearance of the dogs, particularly Jul'fa, upset the rebellious prisoners more than the levelled rifles of the soldiers.

An ultimatum was posed to the rebels: "You have fifteen minutes in which to surrender. Everybody come out and line up. Otherwise the building will be surrounded with straw and set on fire!"

The prisoners replied with angry shouts. They cursed the guards, the administration, the command, the government, Stalin.

A large load of hay was brought up to the barrack, and prisoner workers with sad, tense faces, but with alacrity, began to lay it around the building.

Now not a sound could be heard within the barrack. It was as if there were no one there. A deathly stillness reigned. No one could turn his eyes from the windows and doors of the barricaded building.

Fifteen minutes passed. The silence was suddenly broken by a loud voice calling authoritatively: "Everybody out! I'll count to three . . . One! . . . Two! . . . Three! . . ." Around the building the straw blazed up. The flames leapt higher than the roof, which was made of reeds. It caught fire immediately.

Men began to jump out of the doors and windows of the barrack with raised hands, submissively giving themselves up to the victors. The surrenderers were herded together, led a little way off, and lined up four in a row, under the levelled rifles of a reinforced guard. Now firemen, likewise prisoners, began to put out the fire with primitive hand pumps. Soldiers of the guard assisted them.

Of the two hundred fifty prisoners who had been in the

barrack, fifteen were still missing. Soldiers, covering their faces with the drenched tails of their overcoats which they had filled with snow, would first take a deep breath, hold it, and run into the burning smoke-filled barrack, stay as long as they could without breathing, and drag out the unconscious men. One by one, twelve persons were brought out in this manner. Three persons were still missing. Dogs were sent into the barracks; they balked, rebelled against going into the burning building, and it was necessary to force them. They submitted to discipline unwillingly, following their handlers, snorting, sneezing, rolling their heads.

Jul'fa's handler unleashed her, shouted a command, and ran into the barrack. Jul'fa was not a single pace behind him. She darted into the barrack, paused a moment, sniffed about with some initial confusion, and then disappeared after her master. A bark was heard from inside the barrack, and then the shout of the handler: "Here! To me! Quickly!"

At the shout several soldiers ran into the barrack, and dragged out an unconscious prisoner whom Jul'fa had found. A few seconds later Jul'fa's bark was heard again, and again the shouts of the handler, and the piercing trill of a whistle. The soldiers dragged out still another prisoner. Then the handler jumped out of a window. After him, with a graceful leap, came Jul'fa. The handler, breathing heavily and coughing, wiped his streaming eyes. Jul'fa snorted, shook her head, rubbed her nose in a snowdrift. One prisoner was still missing.

The handler called Jul'fa, and was about to go back into the barrack again, but the camp chief stopped him: "Don't do it! You'll ruin a good dog. To hell with him!"

The handler, glaring angrily, waved him away with his hand. "Jul'fa! Follow me!" he shouted, and jumped back into the barrack through the window.

Two or three minutes passed. Everyone waited tensely and uneasily for the return of Jul'fa and her handler. A bark was heard, and the handler's shout, and then the trill of his whistle. Soldiers ran into the barrack, then came out again carrying the last prisoner. But Jul'fa and her handler did not appear. Then Jul'fa's bark was heard and suddenly she leaped out of the barrack, ran up to the nearest soldier and, seizing his coattail in her teeth, began to drag him after her back into the building. Several other soldiers followed after. She took them to her handler, who was lying unconscious behind the barricaded door. When they carried him out they saw that his overcoat had been torn in several places, on the back and on the sleeves. Jul'fa, in the effort to get him out of the building, had dragged him with her teeth until her strength gave out.

The rebellion was over. The instigators were punished.

IV

Jul'fa remained assigned to search duties in the camp. There was no dog who could match her skill in locating a trail, or in leading the guards to a hidden fugitive, even when snow, rain, fog, or the piercing winds of Kazakhstan had erased all traces from the ground. She excelled all other dogs in her ability to follow a trail which had been obscured by heavy traffic, or where the tracks had been artificially covered.

There are many duties for search dogs in the camps. If a

prisoner fails to show up for work, a dog is given some item of his personal effects to smell, and then led about the area through which he would logically be obliged to pass. The dog smells out the ground, looking for the right scent, and upon finding it, follows it to the place where the wanted person has hidden himself. When supplies are stolen from a warehouse, a dog is brought in. She smells out the scent of the stolen item, follows it, and points out the thief from among other prisoners, even though he be standing in a crowd. The dog finds a stolen article even though it be buried in the ground. Dogs are also employed on terrain searches. Here the objective is to determine whether any person has passed through the area, and if so, in what direction he was travelling, and his present whereabouts. In this type of operation the dog is led about the area and the command to search is repeated continually. The dog follows after her handler, keeping her nose to the ground. Upon finding a trail, she follows it until she comes to its end or until she loses it. If the trail is lost, the dog is again led about the area where she has lost it, until she picks it up again. There are cases, of course, when a trail breaks off and cannot be found again–for example, when the subject of a search enters an automobile, or a train, or mounts a horse. In such cases the dog is helpless.

When the dog locates the person whom she is seeking, she confronts him and barks threateningly, until her handler arrives. She never attacks however, except when commanded to do so, unless he tries to resist or escape. He has only to move however, and she leaps upon him.

Search dogs are trained to recognize whether a man has a weapon in his hand–a club, a knife, a revolver or a rifle–and they are trained to disarm him. They normally do this by seizing the arm above the wrist, and biting until pain makes the victim incapable of using the weapon. In all combat engagements, however, they give first priority to protecting their master, even without being commanded to do so.

In every one of these skills Jul'fa excelled all other search dogs.

A deep mutual attachment and friendship develops between the handlers and their dogs. For years they are inseparable companions, day and night. If the handler becomes ill, the dog does not work during the period of his illness. If the handler's illness is such as to cause protracted absence, his dog is returned to the kennels, and waits there for his return to duty. During this time she is completely isolated. She is given her food through the wire screen, and always by the same attendant, to whom she finally becomes accustomed. The association is limited however, to that incidental to care and feeding. If the handler is separated from the service entirely, then it becomes necessary to undertake a delicate process of transferring the dog to a new handler. This takes about a month—sometimes longer, sometimes shorter, depending on the capability of the dog to develop an attachment to the assigned handler, and upon his ability to develop rapport with her. In the transfer process the old handler continues to work with her during the initial stage, in the presence of the new one. The two men feed the dog together, play with her together, and after a time she becomes somewhat accustomed to the new handler. When this stage is reached, the new handler begins to work with her in the presence of the old one. Later on, the old handler begins unobtrusively to conceal himself from the field of vision of the dog. When she finally becomes accustomed to the new handler, she parts from the old one forever.

The process is not easy for the dogs. They are likely to become listless at first. Sometimes they refuse to obey the commands of the new master, and will not even take food. They are never punished for this however. Devotion—dedication to a master, is esteemed. It can be won only by tenderness.

"I could go on at great length telling of Jul'fa's feats over the years," said the chief of the kennel, continuing his tale, "but search dogs' duties tend to be repetitious. Each operation is much like another—searching out a trail, pursuit, encounter and capture of a violator, a criminal, a fugitive. It's always the same. . . . Jul'fa's reputation is the result of many, many operations in which she participated during her active years. I'm only telling you the most outstanding episodes, those out of the ordinary routine of work."

V

"Jul'fa was already nine years old, which is a considerable age for a dog, when the incident occurred which set her above other dogs for all time. Had it not been for this, she would probably have been retired after a year or two more, depending on her strength and energy.

"It was five years ago, at one of the remote outpost sectors of the camp. A group of prisoners had managed to obtain weapons. They assaulted the guard, and undertook an escape. They did not flee in a group, but took off in various directions, which complicated greatly the task of finding them and rounding them up. For this reason it was necessary to commit a large portion of the guard force to the search operation.

"The flight was discovered late—only toward the evening of the following day, which gave the fugitives an opportunity to disperse in all directions and cover considerable distance. A coordinated search operation was mounted—all over the extensive territory of the camp, and beyond its limits as well, up to a radius of one hundred fifty kilometers. The entire guard force was called out, and all available search dogs were committed. Jul'fa and I, and several other of the best dogs, were posted at the headquarters of the chief of operations. We were held in reserve, and sent out only in case of urgent developments, after which we would return again, awaiting new complications or difficulties with which the others could not cope.

"We enjoyed consistent success, in the face of all kinds of difficulties. Our accomplishments would under ordinary circumstances have meant honors and commendations for us. But, whereas some other handler and his dog would receive an award for some comparatively insignificant deed, Jul'fa and I would not even receive a word of praise for an outstanding performance. 'Why, that's natural for Jul'fa. Nothing at all extraordinary about it. It couldn't have been otherwise. We wouldn't have expected anything else from Jul'fa.' It was hard to bear, of course, but we tried not to show that we were angered by the unfairness of this attitude.

"In order to give a complete account of this attempted escape I would have to relate a whole series of separate episodes, completely unconnected with each other. I am not going to burden you with tales about all these incidents, since not all of them concern our Jul'fa. Suffice it to say that during that uneasy period Jul'fa and I had a tremendous amount of work. Many were the frights we had, and many the dangers we experienced; we didn't win our successes cheaply. Often our assignments were of the most urgent nature. I climbed in the mountains with her, roamed the *steppe*, crawled through mine shafts—searched, pursued, and caught fugitives who had hidden themselves from us. We met resistance, we were shot at; they had armed themselves with knives, stones, clubs—sometimes they fought us with their bare hands. We fought hand to hand, desperately. I would shoot them, Jul'fa would savagely slash at them with her teeth, biting them to death. Jul'fa and I always emerged victorious; we enjoyed continuous success.

"But then, one time, after two weeks of incessant activity, our lucky star fell at last. We had a failure, and it almost cost us our lives. One group of armed fugitives—the principal ringleaders of the flight, had succeeded in getting very far away from the camp. They had made their way as far as Karsakray. At that time the railroad had not yet been put through, and the region was wasteland, very sparsely populated. Karsakray is on the edge of the terrible 'hungry *steppe*'—Bet-Pak-Dala, in which not a living thing is to be found. This group of fugitives had followed the course of the Sary-Su River, whose banks in this area are covered with rich vegetation. Jul'fa and I were part of a pursuit group. After several encounters involving exchanges of fire, the fugitives had succeeded in breaking off contact, and their trail was lost.

"Without going into the details of the search operation, and how we finally picked up the trail again, I'll get to the important part. Jul'fa and I, in the heat of pursuit, committed an unpardonable mistake, one for which we paid dearly. Impelled by the excitement of the chase, following a fresh scent, we moved on quickly, far outdistancing the group which we were accompanying. You see, when a dog is leading the handler along a scent, she runs quickly, and the handler must follow her at a run, holding her on a leash. He runs easily, for the dog pulls him along. Besides, he is lightly armed, and well trained to run. The soldiers, on the other hand, with rifles, full cartridge belts, and packs on their backs, cannot keep up with the dog handler. It is his responsibility to see that he does not become separated from the soldiers accompanying him.

"Jul'fa and I were getting farther and farther away from the others, without noticing it. The terrain along the banks of the Sary-Su is picturesque, covered with bushes. The grass is thick and green. It was early morning, and the air was fresh and cool. One felt exhilaration, and the running was easy. But behind every bush could be danger waiting for us, and death—for Jul'fa and I were alone.

"Jul'fa began to increase her speed. She was no longer smelling the ground. As always when we were approaching the goal, she was now taking the scent directly from the air. I had expended all my strength, and could no longer keep up with her. I began to gasp, and gradually lengthened the leash. Finally I came to the end, and held it by the loop. Now Jul'fa was running ten meters ahead of me. She was pulling so strongly that I couldn't hold the leash any longer. I let go, and helplessly came to a stop, trying to recover my breath. Jul'fa leaped on ahead. She jumped into the bushes and began to fight with someone, tearing and snapping with her teeth. I started to her aid, but suddenly two men jumped out of the bushes in front of me. They had revolvers in their hands and rifles slung across their backs. I didn't know what to do. I levelled my pistol at them. Glancing back however, I saw that there was no one in sight. I had left my own people far behind.

"The fugitives did not want to shoot me, fearing that the sound of the shots would betray their location. And for my part, confronted as I was by two armed men with revolvers aimed at me, I didn't want to fire either, since I did not know how many more of my opponents there might be in the vicinity. A few paces from me, in the bushes, Jul'fa's battle continued. I could clearly hear each of her breaths; I heard her angry snarling and knew that she was already overpowering her opponent. Suddenly she yelped in fury, and began to engage another enemy.

"One of the men standing before me said, 'Don't shout, and don't fire, or you're a dead man! Call off your dog, you snake!'

"I called Jul'fa. She emerged from the shrubbery, covered with blood, and came up to me. A bloody foam was trickling from her mouth, and a wound in her side was bleeding freely. She looked at our foes standing in front of me, and awaited my command to attack. I was powerless to give it.

"A third person came out of the shrubbery now, holding a rifle in his hands. He was bleeding, and his clothes were tattered and bloodsoaked. He was breathing with difficulty. 'She's bitten me to death, the damned Bloody Nicholas! I stabbed her with a bayonet, the vermin! But she wouldn't let go. She's torn me to pieces!'

"They ordered me to throw down my revolver. I obeyed. One of the fugitives came over and picked it up. They took away my cartridge belt. Then they asked me where the soldiers were, and I said that they were following me.

"Suddenly I felt a kind of blow from behind, and something sharp and cold plunged deeply into my back. My head whirled, I couldn't stand on my legs, I fell. As if in a dream I saw Jul'fa leap upon someone behind me. Snarling, she began to tear at him. There were shots, and something heavy struck me in the breast. I passed out. . . .

"When I regained consciousness I was in the hospital. It was not until much later, when I had fully recovered, that they told me what had happened to Jul'fa. She had been stabbed by a bayonet and had received two bullet wounds while protecting me. One of them damaged her leg seriously. The sound of the shots had led our soldiers to the scene, but upon arrival they found only a dead man whom Jul'fa had killed, and another one, dying, whom Jul'fa, despite her loss of blood, had torn with her teeth, even though she was too weak to stand on her legs. I was found lying unconscious, shot through the chest and stabbed in the back with a knife. The fugitives had fled, but they were found not far away, and captured after a prolonged exchange of fire and a savage hand-to-hand fight. Jul'fa was permanently injured. . . .

"Her loss was kept a closely guarded secret. With great difficulty and at considerable expense, a double for her was found and brought to the camp. The similarity was truly startling; it was extremely difficult to tell the false Jul'fa from the true one. The double was younger, yet her movements were not so energetic, and she lacked the sedateness and self-confidence which were inherent in Jul'fa. The best instructors were assigned to the new dog. They worked intensively with her, and taught her the most complicated of operational techniques—brought her to the highest level of development. In the end she turned out to be an outstanding search dog. In no way, however, could she compare with Jul'fa. There simply aren't any dogs like Jul'fa. . . .

"For a long time the false Jul'fa was able to accomplish the role of the real one simply by her presence alone. It was strictly forbidden, however, to use the double on complicated operations. The slightest blunder could tear down Jul'fa's priceless prestige. But despite the jealous guarding of the secret, the truth finally leaked out. The news spread like wildfire throughout the camp. The prisoners rejoiced—and yet there was regret, as well.

"The counterfeit was also named Jul'fa."

After this last unfortunate adventure Jul'fa's master, after several months in the hospital, received a promotion in the form of appointment as chief of the kennels. The crippled Jul'fa went with him.

* * *

On the eve of my departure the chief of the kennels invited me to visit his home. He took me to a small detached cottage. In the garden which surrounded it three little children were playing, and with them was a beautiful German shepherd, the property of my host. The children were pulling her tail with all their might, tugging at her ears, clutching her long smooth fur, putting their little hands into her mouth, unceremoniously poking their fingers into her eyes, her ears, her nose, with the thoughtless cruelty of children, doing whatever they wished with her. And the dog was enduring it all, patiently tolerating them. Now and then she would whine softly, when it was especially painful for her. When she walked among the children she stepped very carefully, in order not to upset them, or hit them with her leg, or hurt them in any way.

"Aren't you afraid the dog may bite the children? They are trying her patience so with their pranks," I said.

"Why, what do you mean? She'd never bite them! It's a matter of training, influencing her instincts," he answered.

"Yes, indeed," I thought, remembering what he had been telling me all afternoon, "training. What can't an animal be made to do and endure by means of training!—And not only animals, it would seem."

VLADIMIR ANDREYEV

Vladimir Andreyev, a former Soviet career officer, served for several years in the operational forces of the NKVD, and through service in posts of increasing responsibility rose to the rank of lieutenant colonel. Today he is a political emigre living in western Europe, where he is engaged in research on special aspects of the Soviet system. His works have been published in the United States and in Europe. In addition he has contributed studies to several institutes and universities.

In 1951, Andreyev participated as a witness in the trial called by the International Tribunal in Brussels against the Soviet concentration camp system. The western European press accorded considerable attention to the testimony provided by Mr. Andreyev, and the Communist press demanded his surrender to the Soviet Union for trial and punishment—for desertion to the West and for his activity against the Communist regime.

In October, 1952 Vladimir Andreyev presented a detailed report concerning Soviet concentration camps to a special committee of the United Nations, which was entered in the official record in 1953. In subsequent years Mr. Andreyev has frequently served as consultant to the International Commission on matters pertaining to the Soviet camps.

Andreyev's works are not fictional. They portray incidents which actually took place and which are known to the author through personal observation—from investigative reports and other operational documents to which he had free access at the time, or from personal contact with the actual participants in the experiences described. The times and places of the incidents, and the names of the participants are factual, except for minor personalities whose names were unknown to the author.

The name Vladimir Andreyev is the pseudonym under which the author participated in the proceedings of the International Commission, and through which his writings have become known to a world-wide audience.